W9-BTF-836

SIMPLE SUCCESS
The Nutrisystem® Guide to Healthy Eating

SIMPLE SUCCESS

The Nutrisystem® Guide to Healthy Eating

By the Research and Development Team at Nutrisystem, Inc.

With select recipes from
The New Glucose Revolution Low GI Family Cookbook
and *The New Glucose Revolution Life Plan*

Foreword by Joanna McMillan

Da Capo
∞
LIFE
LONG
A Member of the
Perseus Books Group

Copyright © 2012 by Nutrisystem®

Nutrisystem authors: Karen Curtis, MPH, RD; Meghan Nichols, RD; with recipe and culinary contributions from Max Sugarman.

Recipes on pages 41, 44, 47–48, 57, 68, 71–72, 84–85, 92–94, 97–98, 100, 102, 105, 124–138: *The New Glucose Revolution Low GI Family Cookbook;* Dr. Jennie Brand-Miller, Kaye Foster-Powell and Anneka Manning, with Philippa Sandall. Recipe on page 77 from *The New Glucose Revolution Life Plan;* Dr. Jennie Brand-Miller, Johanna Burani, and Kaye Foster-Powell.

Photographs on pages 13, 45, 46, 56, 70, 86, 90, 95, 101, 104, 125, 126, 131, 135, 136, 139, 145, 146, 151, and 154 courtesy of Hachette
All other photographs by DePersico Group

All rights reserved. No part of this publication may be reproduced, stored in a retrieval system, or transmitted, in any form or by any means, electronic, mechanical, photocopying, recording, or otherwise, without the prior written permission of the publisher. Printed in the United States of America. For information, address Da Capo Press, 44 Farnsworth Street, 3rd Floor, Boston, MA 02210.

Designed by Jill Shaffer
Set in 11 point Avenir by Eclipse Publishing Services

Cataloging-in-Publication data for this book is available from the Library of Congress.

First Da Capo Press edition 2012
ISBN: 978-0-7382-1640-9 (paperback)

Published by Da Capo Press
A Member of the Perseus Books Group
www.dacapopress.com

Note: The information in this book is true and complete to the best of our knowledge. This book is intended only as an informative guide for those wishing to know more about cooking in a healthy way using Nutrisystem® tools and tips. In no way is this book intended to replace, countermand, or conflict with the advice given to you by your own physician. The ultimate decision concerning care should be made between you and your doctor. We strongly recommend you follow his or her advice. Information in this book is general and is offered with no guarantees on the part of the authors or Da Capo Press. The authors and publisher disclaim all liability in connection with the use of this book.

Da Capo Press books are available at special discounts for bulk purchases in the U.S. by corporations, institutions, and other organizations. For more information, please contact the Special Markets Department at the Perseus Books Group, 2300 Chestnut Street, Suite 200, Philadelphia, PA, 19103, or call (800) 810-4145, ext. 5000, or e-mail special.markets@perseusbooks.com.

10 9 8 7 6 5 4 3

To every reader on his or her journey to healthy eating

CONTENTS

FOREWORD

Congratulations for picking up this book and committing to a healthier lifestyle and a happier you! We both know that it is really hard to get the weight off—and keep it off. One of the reasons so many of us have trouble is that we succumb to the latest fad diet or extreme exercise approach, then consider ourselves failures when a few weeks or months down the line we're back to square one, unable to keep it up. Well we've got news for you: you can forget the quick fix programs, forget the dramatic promises, and don't waste your money on those miracle supplements or exercise equipment with persuasive ads promising you a new body. You don't need them and they don't work. What *does* work is changing the way you eat, the way you move, and the way you think about food for life. That's it—that's the big secret. And the Nutrisystem® program will help you do just that.

Nutrisystem is one of the best weight loss programs I have seen. Why? Because it seeks to teach you the best, most nutritious foods to eat, in the right proportions for your needs, and it embraces the best scientific evidence we have to date on how we should eat. No food groups are eliminated. You don't need to count calories. You won't be cutting out carbs, so you'll have the energy to exercise, and you'll be eating truly delicious nutritious food. In short, it teaches you how to eat. It is not a diet but a way of eating that you will learn how to sustain for the rest of your life. With healthy eating comes a healthy, well-nourished body that gives you the best platform for lowering your risk of chronic lifestyle-related disease.

I spent five years researching the impact of protein, carbohydrate, and the glycemic index (GI) on body composition change (body fat and muscle changes) and cardiovascular risk factors. What my studies and those of others have clearly shown is that a low GI diet is important for good health and does indeed help you obtain a better body composition. Your body takes time to digest low GI foods and needs to produce less insulin to deal with these foods, and as a result the metabolic impact on your body is reduced. We are not designed to deal with large amounts of high GI foods, and it is for this reason that carbs have gotten a bad name. But by choosing "SmartCarbs" you can enjoy these foods without the downfall. The best carbs also provide fiber, crucial for gut health, and nutrients essential for good health. Low GI SmartCarbs provide us with a tool for picking the best. The Nutrisystem® program combines these foods with essential protein-rich foods and those providing healthy fats. The result is an optimal diet that will have you firing on all cylinders . . . what I call your inner mojo!

So congratulations on making the right step toward a healthier, happier you. I wish you all the best on your weight loss journey and urge you to commit to this way of living for life.

Warm regards,
Dr. Joanna McMillan
Registered Nutritionist & Accredited Practicing Dietitian
Sydney, Australia

INTRODUCTION

◄ A colorful array of SmartCarbs shows the variety of nutritious eating choices.

1

NUTRISYSTEM: YOUR PARTNER IN WEIGHT MANAGEMENT

Congratulations on choosing Nutrisystem as your weight management partner! The Nutrisystem® program is not just a diet; it's a healthy, low glycemic index (GI) approach to eating that utilizes a learn-by-doing method. By following the program, you learn how to make healthy food choices in the right portion sizes to nourish your body while you control your hunger and meet your weight management goal. In addition, Nutrisystem will provide you with the tools and resources you need to help you continue this way of healthy eating and living.

Simple Success: The Nutrisystem® Guide to Healthy Eating is your essential resource as you navigate healthy eating with or without Nutrisystem® foods. The Nutrisystem program teaches you what types and portions of foods to eat, and now you can utilize these skills to do it on your own. You can continue to practice portion control, which is necessary for weight management, while sharing healthy, home-cooked meals with family and friends.

When used in combination with Nutrisystem® Transition and Maintenance plans, this guide can help you successfully manage your weight long term. As you approach your weight loss goal, our flexible plans allow you to incorporate Nutrisystem® foods every day or every so often, depending on your lifestyle and personal needs. (Though keep in mind that the fewer perfectly portioned Nutrisystem foods you use, the more support and guidance you may need along the way.)

This book will show you the types and amounts of food you should be eating each day, depending on your weight management goal. *If you are still intending to lose weight*, follow your current Nutrisystem *Daily Planner*, substituting the recipes from the book for your Nutrisystem® entrées and/or SmartCarb or PowerFuel additions. Most people typically lose one to two pounds per week while following the Nutrisystem program; however, your rate of weight loss may occasionally vary due to changes in your eating or activity habits. **This is why regularly monitoring your weight is so important.**

If you are beginning to transition to weight maintenance or if you are currently maintaining your weight, you will likely need to increase the amount of food or calories you consume, compared to your weight loss phase. Finding your perfect balance of food intake and physical activity needed to maintain your weight may take some figuring out. Weigh yourself at least weekly and use the guidelines on page 153 to adjust your food intake and/or amount of physical activity to meet your weight management goal. Keep in mind, these are only guidelines, and your individual experience may differ. If you need further help or assistance, contact a Nutrisystem counselor or visit www.nutrisystem.com.

> Nutrisystem is a program that teaches you about the right kinds of food to eat…I like to think of it as more of a lifestyle change.
> —CORA M.

THE BENEFITS OF MANAGING WEIGHT

You may have heard your doctor or other healthcare professional tell you to "lose some weight." And you probably know why: maintaining a healthy weight is important for good health. But that's just part of the story. Losing weight can have many positive physical and emotional health benefits.

For example, losing just 5 to 10% of your body weight (10 to 20 pounds for a 200-pound person) can significantly improve your health, help you better manage a chronic disease, or possibly reduce your risk for developing chronic disease. In general, losing weight may result in:

- **Lower blood sugar** for a person with diabetes or the prevention or delay in developing diabetes for someone at risk
- **Lower blood pressure** and possible reduced need for blood pressure medication
- **Lower blood cholesterol and triglycerides,** which can lower risk for heart disease and stroke
- **Improved asthma control** and possible decrease in asthma medication use
- **Improved sleep quality** and decreased daytime sleepiness for those suffering from sleep apnea

Not only can controlling your weight improve your health, but it may also improve your well-being and outlook on life. Participants in the National Weight Control Registry who lost weight and maintained their weight loss reported:

- Improved energy levels
- Improved mobility
- Better general mood
- Greater self-confidence

Here's a helpful tip. Figure out your reason(s) for wanting to lose weight and your motivation for keeping it off. Write your reasons down and let them be your source of inspiration throughout your journey! Keep a running list of all the benefits of regaining control over your weight as you experience them. We're sure you'll find the benefits greatly outweigh the ease of not trying!

WHY NUTRISYSTEM WORKS

Nutrisystem offers a low GI program that is based on proven, safe, and effective weight management strategies and meets national nutrition and health guidelines. In addition, we provide the structure, support, and self-monitoring tools that can make it easier to stay on track and acquire lasting healthy habits. In short, we've designed our system to be one you can stick with long term.

The Nutrisystem weight management approach is based on the following proven principles:

1 Balanced, low GI nutrition
2 Convenient structure and portion control
3 Active living
4 Access to resources and support

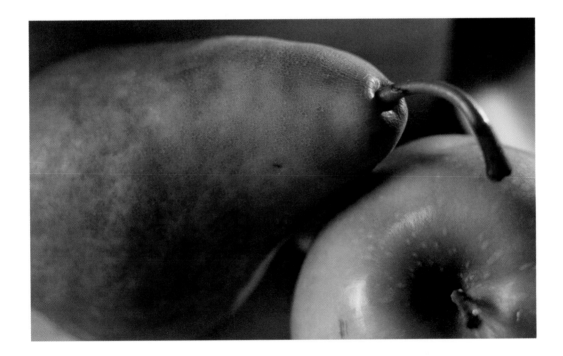

BALANCED, LOW GI NUTRITION

Eating fewer calories than you burn is the most important component of a successful weight loss program. However, eliminating certain food groups or foods from your diet can limit important nutrients your body needs for good health. That's why Nutrisystem takes the balanced nutritional approach to weight management. Our low GI program offers an ideal combination of lean protein, high-fiber carbohydrates, and heart-healthy fats. You can feel confident knowing our program meets national nutrition guidelines for healthy eating.

Our program provides simple guidance for making healthy food choices to complement your Nutrisystem® meals and/or to follow a low GI diet without Nutrisystem® foods. Our three simple-to-understand categories—SmartCarbs, PowerFuels, and Vegetables—group foods based on their nutrient content so you can easily achieve a healthy and nutritionally balanced diet. Additionally, we provide guidance on low-calorie Extras, like condiments and spices, which can add some pizzazz to your meal plan.

- **SmartCarbs:** These are nutrient-dense, low glycemic index (GI) carbohydrate-containing foods like whole grains and fruit that keep you satisfied throughout the day.
- **PowerFuels:** Lean proteins and healthy fats including fish, chicken, and nuts take longer to digest, which helps combat hunger.
- **Vegetables:** Enjoy at least four servings of nonstarchy vegetables per day—but you can eat as many as you want! This offers you a low-calorie way to fight cravings while you reduce your risk of developing certain chronic diseases.

Nutrisystem gave me a new way of thinking. I've continued to lose weight through exercise as well as using the principles of a low-GI diet that Nutrisystem taught me."
—JONELLE B.

SmartCarbs: Low GI, Nutrient-Rich Carbohydrates

SmartCarbs are nutrient-dense, fiber-rich, low glycemic index (GI) carbohydrate-containing foods, like many whole grains and fruits, which help keep you satisfied throughout the day. SmartCarbs are carbohydrate sources that are digested more slowly (low GI), keeping you fuller longer, and that promote good health by delivering vitamins, minerals, fiber, and other important nutrients. While refined carbohydrates from white bread, white rice, and other refined grains, pastries, sugared sodas, and other highly processed foods are OK on occasion, overeating this type of carbohydrate may contribute to weight gain, interfere with weight loss, and possibly promote diabetes and heart disease.

Below are tips to help you choose SmartCarbs.

- Make at least one of your daily SmartCarbs servings a fruit serving. However, limit 100% fruit juice intake to one cup per week.
- Check the nutrition facts label and aim to get 1 to 3 grams of fiber per serving of SmartCarbs.
- Choose whole grains whenever possible. Look for whole wheat, oat, rye, brown or wild rice, bulgur, barley, amaranth, millet, quinoa, and/or sorghum as one of the top three ingredients listed on the food label. Products that are made only with 100% whole grains are the best choice. These foods typically offer more fiber and higher amounts of vitamins and minerals.

Understanding the Glycemic Index (GI)

The glycemic index (GI) is a feature of the Nutrisystem® program that in conjunction with our portion-controlled and structured meal plans can offer additional health and weight loss benefits. The glycemic index is a measure of the quality of a carbohydrate-containing food and its impact on your blood sugar levels—or how quickly it enters your blood stream. High GI foods (typically refined grains) are broken down quickly by the body and cause a quick and sudden increase in blood sugar and insulin (a hormone that promotes fat storage), followed by an abrupt decline. This may ultimately lead to feelings of fatigue and hunger. Foods with a lower GI (whole grains, legumes, and most fruits)

cause a slower and steadier rise in blood sugar with a more gradual decline, because they take longer for the body to break down. Therefore, these types of foods may help you feel fuller longer and may help you avoid overeating or making poor food choices. This is especially important when managing your weight. For people with diabetes, this could mean better blood sugar control, which combined with weight loss, could mean less medication use and reduced risk for developing diabetes complications.

Keep in mind, GI is only one piece of the weight management puzzle. The combination of a low GI diet along with portion control, structured eating, regular physical activity, and adequate support is truly what makes the Nutrisystem® program work.

SMARTCARBS SERVING SIZE GUIDELINES   SC

1 EACH	1 CUP
medium fruit (or 2 small fruit)	berries
slice of whole grain bread	grapes
small whole grain roll	cut/canned fruit
4 to 6-inch whole grain tortilla/wrap	
English muffin (whole grain)	

½ CUP	¼ CUP
cooked rice or pasta	dried fruits
cooked grains	whole grain crackers
cereals	hummus
starchy vegetables (beans, peas, corn, potatoes, parsnips, winter squash)	
100% fruit juice	

PowerFuels: Focus on Protein and Heart-Healthy Fats

PowerFuels are the sources of lean proteins and healthy fats that are an essential component to a healthy diet, especially while managing weight. Protein is the building block of our bodies. It is important to every function, including building muscle, repairing tissue, and maintaining healthy immunity. But it can also aid in your weight management efforts. While you manage your weight, a higher-protein diet has been shown to help:

- Increase satiety, so you feel less hungry after a meal.
- Promote greater fullness—helping you feel satisfied and possibly making you less likely to make poor choices or overeat.
- Retain lean body or muscle mass. When you lose weight, you lose both fat and muscle. An adequate protein intake can help you retain muscle mass, which is critical for optimal calorie burning.
- Maintain weight loss better compared to a low-protein diet, especially when combined with a low glycemic index (GI) diet.

An adequate amount of healthy fats in your diet is also important for satiety, which is helpful when managing weight. In addition, fat makes food taste good. Keep in mind, fat is a more concentrated source of calories, so enjoy it in moderation. Overconsumption of some types of fat may actually increase your risk for heart disease. Therefore, limit sources of saturated fats and avoid trans fats, and concentrate on sources of unsaturated fats. To further reduce risk for heart disease, aim for two servings of fatty fish per week.

> I am eating healthier and exercising, and I've also learned to control my mind and not let my mind control me—I control what foods or drinks I put in my mouth.
>
> —MARY L.

Keep the following tips in mind as you choose PowerFuels

- Limit egg yolks to two per week. Egg yolks are high in saturated fat and cholesterol, which may have a negative impact on cardiovascular health.
- Look for lean cuts of meat like chicken, turkey, sirloins, tenderloins, top loins, roasts, and top rounds. These cuts offer more protein and less fat per serving, making them more heart-healthy choices.
- Choose low-sodium (140 mg or less per serving) or reduced-sodium meats and cheeses where available. An increased sodium intake may increase your risk for developing high blood pressure, heart disease, and/or kidney disease.
- Aim to get at least two PowerFuel servings each week from a fatty fish source. Fatty fish are rich in omega-3 fatty acids, which may reduce your risk for heart disease, stroke, and depression.
- Combine nuts and nut butters with seeds or grains to create a complete protein (e.g., peanut butter and whole grain bread, nuts sprinkled over rice/pasta-based dishes like Nutrisystem® Asian Beef Entrée, or nuts and sunflower seeds combined in a trail mix).

POWERFUELS SERVING SIZE GUIDELINES

1 EACH	1 CUP
egg	fat-free or low-fat (1%) milk
2-ounce portion of lean meats	low-fat yogurt
2-ounce portion of fatty fish (salmon, tuna, mackerel, swordfish, trout)	nonfat cottage cheese
3-ounce portion of shellfish or fish (or ½ cup canned)	egg substitute
1 ounce string cheese or snack cheese	egg whites

½ CUP	¼ CUP
tofu	shredded light cheese or 1 slice (reduced sodium)
soybeans	
shredded soy cheese/nonfat cheese or 2 slices (reduced sodium)	

1 TABLESPOON	2 TABLESPOONS
nut butters (peanut, almond, cashew, etc.)	nuts

A colorful array of PowerFuels shows the variety of eating choices. ▶

Vegetables: Four or More

Most Americans do not eat an adequate amount of vegetables. This could be putting our health at risk. An adequate intake of vegetables may reduce your risk for developing cardiovascular disease, high blood pressure, and some forms of cancer. Vegetables provide essential nutrients such as vitamins, minerals, and phytochemicals that enhance health. Additionally, substituting vegetables for higher-calorie foods can be a very effective weight management strategy. Because most vegetables are high in fiber and water content, they tend to fill you up more easily, which can certainly help when managing weight.

Strive for vegetable color variety as well. Choose from green, red, purple, white, yellow, and orange vegetables to ensure you are getting the different nutrients and phytochemicals that each group offers. Fresh and frozen vegetables, without added sauces, are great choices. Canned vegetables, which are sometimes higher in sodium and lower in nutrients, can also be enjoyed on occasion; just be sure to look for reduced-sodium varieties.

> * Keep in mind, starchy vegetables including beans, peas, corn, potatoes (regular and sweet), parsnips, and winter squash count as SmartCarb servings, as they offer more carbohydrates and calories than a typical vegetable serving.

VEGETABLES SERVING SIZE GUIDELINES	VG
1 CUP	**½ CUP**
nonstarchy vegetables	cooked nonstarchy vegetables
	low-sodium vegetable juice

Nutrisystem is different because it teaches you how to eat healthily."
—MELODY H.

To help make sure you get enough vegetables each day, consider all "nonstarchy" vegetables unlimited, but ensure you get at least four servings per day.

- Top whole grain toast with a slice of fresh tomato.
- Include mushrooms, onions, tomatoes, and spinach in a morning omelet.
- Top your Nutrisystem® pizza with broccoli, zucchini, fresh tomatoes, mushrooms, peppers, or any of your other favorite vegetables.

- Chop up raw veggies and enjoy as an afternoon snack with fat-free ranch dip.
- Make a soup and salad combo, combining one of our delicious soups with at least a cup of salad greens or raw vegetables.
- Add sliced cucumbers, tomatoes, and lettuce to sandwiches. Or instead of a sandwich, enjoy lean meats and low-fat cheeses on a bed of salad greens.
- Mix in vegetables with foods you already love. For example, combine cooked broccoli florets with pasta, add spinach to your favorite soup, like Nutrisystem® Italian Wedding Soup.

Extras

Extras are optional no-calorie or low-calorie add-ins that can add a little pizzazz to your meal plan without thwarting your weight loss efforts! Choose unlimited quantities of calorie-free items (10 calories or less per serving). Limit foods that contain up to 35 calories per serving to no more than three servings daily. Below are some hints on incorporating Extras.

- Try three cups of air-popped popcorn to satisfy a snack craving (three Extras).
- Combine unlimited vegetables with low-sodium broth as a snack or to add volume to a meal.
- Top 1 cup of sugar-free gelatin with 1 tablespoon of sugar-free whipped topping to satisfy your sweet tooth (two Extras).

Use spices and seasoning to add a punch of flavor to your Nutrisystem® entrées:

- Red pepper flakes, basil, garlic powder, and oregano go great with Italian dishes.
- Cilantro and cumin complement Spanish dishes well.
- Add low-sodium soy sauce, ginger, and garlic to Asian dishes.

Note: Be cautious of sodium in marinades and condiments; look for low- and reduced-sodium ways to spice up your food.

EXTRAS SERVING SIZE GUIDELINES (OPTIONAL) EX

UNLIMITED	LIMITED—MAX OF 3 SERVINGS/DAY
spices/seasonings (salt-free)	1 cup popcorn
low-sodium broths	1 cup sugar-free gelatin
calorie-free sweeteners	1 tablespoon sugar-free syrups/toppings/honeys
calorie-free beverages (unsweetened coffee, tea, diet soda)	1 tablespoon fat-free dressings
fresh/dried herbs	1 tablespoon reduced-sodium condiments, salsas, and marinades
lemon/lime juice	1 tablespoon fat-free creamer
	1 tablespoon reduced-fat or fat-free cream cheese
	1 teaspoon seeds
	1 teaspoon oil (olive, canola, peanut, flax, vegetable)

CONVENIENT STRUCTURE AND PORTION CONTROL

Portion control is an integral part of weight loss success. Being mindful of portion sizes helps cut excess calories, which helps you manage your weight. In addition, eating smaller portions more frequently throughout the day may actually help control hunger, making it easier to stay on track.

Nutrisystem offers flexible, user-friendly plans that make it simple to determine when, what, and how much to eat. Then we show you when and how to compliment your Nutrisystem® entrées with healthy foods, allowing you to eat often for hunger control and to learn more healthy habits. The Nutrisystem® Transition and Maintenance Programs encourage you to put your new healthy eating knowledge and skills into practice with a menu of programs that allow you to eat Nutrisystem® foods every day, most days, or just once in awhile.

As you continue on your weight management journey, keep in mind the following guidelines you learned on the Nutrisystem® program:

- **Eat breakfast:** Breakfast is truly the most important meal of the day. It can help boost your energy levels and stave off mid-morning hunger.
- **Snack sensibly:** Choosing a small snack that is low-fat and rich in protein and/or fiber can help control cravings between meals. SmartCarbs like whole fruit or whole grain crackers or cereal make great snacks since they offer fiber to help fill you up. Low-fat milk, yogurt, cheese, nuts, and nut butters are PowerFuels that make a great protein-rich snack.
- **Eat every three to four hours:** Enjoy three small meals and two to three small snacks per day. Eating small amounts frequently can help you feel more satisfied between meals.

> Nutrisystem has helped me a lot with the mindset you need to learn to eat in a healthy way.
> —JIM B.

ACTIVE LIVING

Regular physical activity is an important component in weight management and overall health and wellness. While regular activity helps you burn calories during the weight loss phase, it is even more important to your success as you approach your goal weight. Research suggests that many individuals that have experienced a significant weight loss may need to increase the amount and/or intensity of their daily activity in order to maintain their weight loss. Therefore, as you approach your goal weight, begin to increase the amount of activity or the intensity of the activity so you can continue to burn the amount of calories needed to maintain your weight.

There are many other physical, mental, and emotional benefits of regular physical activity. Just thirty minutes a day of moderate activity can help you improve your short- and long-term health and wellness. Below is a list of some of the benefits of regular physical activity.

- **Improved energy level:** Regular activity supports good cardiovascular health, which means your body is functioning more efficiently. In addition, people who exercise regularly tend to sleep better and feel more rested.
- **Improved mental health:** Physical activity can reduce risk for depression, enhance mood, and improve brain function.
- **Reduced risk for chronic disease:** Being active can reduce your risk for developing cardiovascular disease, stroke, diabetes, and even some forms of cancer.
- **Improved bone health:** Weight-bearing exercises, like walking or weight training, can help strengthen muscles and bone, reducing the risk for falls and breaks.

How Much Activity Do I Need?

The 2008 Physical Activity Guidelines for Americans recommends that healthy adults achieve at least 150 minutes of moderate-intensity physical activity each week and participate in strengthening activities that work all of the major muscle groups two days per week.

However, you don't need to do this activity all at once. Finding three 10-minute increments each day may be easier for you to achieve and delivers the same health benefits. For example, you could walk the dog for ten minutes before work, take a ten-minute walk at lunch, and take a ten-minute bike ride in the evening. The Nutrisystem® My Daily 3 program helps you determine your current activity levels and interests and provides sample activity plans to help you get started and stay motivated to stick with it.

✶ **Always speak with your doctor or healthcare professional before beginning any new activity or exercise program.**

If you are extremely active, you may require more calories, even if you are trying to lose weight. Contact a Nutrisystem counselor who can help you adjust your meal plan.

Moderate activity is defined as activity that:

- Is equivalent to a 3 mph brisk walk
- Raises your heart rate 50 to 70% of your maximum heart rate
- Permits you to talk but not sing

Vigorous activities also count! Vigorous activity is defined as activity that:

- Is equivalent to a 5 mph or greater jog or run
- Raises your heart rate 70 to 85% of your maximum heart rate
- Makes it difficult to speak more than a few words without taking a breath

One minute of vigorous activity is equivalent to two minutes of moderate activity. Don't forget to incorporate strength training that works all major muscle groups—upper body, core, and lower body—two days per week.

Ten ways to get more active throughout the day:

1. Get to work early and walk ten minutes around the parking lot or building.

2. Get off the bus or train one stop early and walk the rest of the way.

3. Park farther away at the mall or shopping center and walk from store to store.

4. Use ten minutes of your lunch break to go for a brisk walk.

5. Make family time active time—go for a walk or dance to your favorite tunes.

6. Take the stairs instead of the elevator whenever you can.

7. Walk across your office to speak to a coworker instead of sending that e-mail.

8. Do short errands by foot instead of by car.

9. Get active during TV commercial breaks.

10. Carry your grocery bags into the house one by one.

RESOURCES AND SUPPORT

Studies have shown that dieters who have a source of support tend to be more successful. Nutrisystem® wants you to be successful and recognizes the importance of having support throughout the process of weight loss and weight maintenance. Since each person is different, Nutrisystem offers a variety of support options including trained counselors, online resources and trackers, an online community of support, and grocery and dining out guides. In addition, Nutrisystem offers carefully selected products, tools, cookbooks, and nutritional supplements that can complement your Nutrisystem experience. To learn more, visit www.nutrisystem.com.

DINING OUT AND GROCERY FOOD GUIDES	Included in your Resource Guide and available online: www.nutrisystem.com
MINDSET MAKEOVER® GUIDE	This week-by-week online guide will help you learn the skills essential for long-term weight control; create winning attitudes and habits through this gradual, realistic approach Discover what to change, how to change it, and how to make it last Includes: expert advice, video testimonials, tutorials, quizzes, polls, tips, and insightful weight management information
ONLINE ARTICLES AND TIPS	Includes: online recipe center, biweekly newsletters, daily tips, library of articles and tips, success stories, and corporate blog
ONLINE TRACKING TOOLS	Includes: Weight and Measurement Log, Food Log, My Daily 3 Log, and Water Intake Log
NUTRISYSTEM SMART PHONE APP	Access to the Nutrisystem® menu, as well as all online tracking tools on-the-go
NUTRISYSTEM ONLINE COMMUNITY	Includes: community groups, chat rooms, discussion boards, member blogs, e-classes, and social media like Facebook and Twitter
COUNSELING SERVICES	Access to trained counselors who can successfully guide you through your weight management journey

WHAT'S FOR

Creating a palate-pleasing, nutritionally balanced plate using the fundamentals of the Nutrisystem program can be easier than you think. The balanced Nutrisystem plate consists of high-fiber SmartCarbs, protein-packed PowerFuels, and colorful, filling Vegetables. This combination ensures you get the proper balance of nutrients to keep you full and satisfied as you maximize fiber, vitamin, and mineral intake—and minimize fat and excess calorie intake.

What should your plate look like? The diagram on the next page illustrates the composition of a healthy, balanced plate. Fill half of your plate with vegetables prepared with minimal oils or salt. The other half of your plate will be evenly divided by appropriate portions of both PowerFuels and SmartCarbs. Again, prepare foods with minimal fat and salt. Instead, use salt-free spice rubs, marinades, or light sauces (Optional Extras) to enhance the natural flavors of the foods. Best of all, you can apply this concept to any meal!

Keep in mind, portion control is critical to weight control. An overconsumption of calories, no matter what the source, will ultimately lead to weight gain. So follow the guidelines in your Grocery Guide and use your portion control tools so you can properly portion the PowerFuel, SmartCarb, and Extras selections you choose.

DINNER?
basic plating 101

This section is set up to help you build healthy meals around PowerFuels you would likely find in your pantry, fridge, or freezer. This pictorial guide will help you visualize the composition of your plate with the proper portions of PowerFuels, SmartCarbs, Veggies, and even Extras. We then provide you with tips for preparing poultry, beef, pork, fish, salads, and vegetarian options so that they are healthy, delicious, and filling. You will also find tips for how to add low-calorie Extras in the form of simple spice rubs, marinades, or light sauces that bring out the natural flavors of your favorite dishes. Each section will also include suggested quick and healthy SmartCarbs and Veggies to complement each PowerFuel. Looking for even more ideas? Check out the Suggested Pantry List on page 148.

 SMARTCARBS should comprise approximately one-fourth of your plate.

 POWERFUELS should comprise approximately one-fourth of your plate.

 Nonstarchy **VEGETABLES** should comprise **at least** half of your plate.

 Optional **EXTRAS** can be added to the other three categories.

Italian-seasoned chicken breast, mashed sweet potatoes, and green beans sprinkled with chopped walnuts

POULTRY

Healthy Preparation

Chicken and turkey are lean meats and, therefore, can dry out more easily during cooking. Choose cooking methods that help preserve the moisture of the meat. Searing the meat first can help retain some of the natural juices during the cooking process. Sear the outside of the meat over high heat and then cook in oven until the internal temperature reaches at least 165°F.

- **Grilling:** Sear the meat a minute or two on each side over high heat to help retain the juices and then move to another area of the grill to finish cooking. Or marinate lean cuts in low-fat marinades for up to a few hours before grilling to add additional moisture. Spice rubs and dipping sauces can also add great flavor to grilled chicken.
- **Baking:** Marinades and brines can help lean cuts stay moist during the baking process. Baste the meat with marinating liquids throughout the baking process.
- **Roasting:** Roasting chicken with the skin on also allows it to retain its juiciness; just remove skin before eating. Top warm or chilled roast chicken slices with low-fat sauces such as fruit compotes.

Grilled chicken and vegetable skewers, corn on the cob, and grilled vegetables

Barbeque chicken drumsticks, brown rice, and grilled zucchini and red peppers

SAUCE SUGGESTIONS	GREAT RUBS FOR POULTRY	SIMPLE MARINADES
Cold salsas or warm tomato sauces work well with chicken breast	Chili powder, cumin, and garlic on chicken add a southwestern flair	Dijon mustard, lemon, and garlic infuse flavor to both chicken and turkey
Fruit compotes, like cranberry or orange, complement turkey	Thyme, rosemary, garlic, and fresh ground pepper nicely flavor turkey cutlets	Low-fat Italian dressing is a quick and easy flavor enhancer

Suggested Pairings

The mild flavor of poultry pairs well with sweet vegetables and starches. If you're grilling chicken, throw a variety of vegetables on the grill as well. Below are some pairings to try.

POWERFUEL	SMARTCARB	VEGETABLE
Sliced roasted turkey	Baked sweet potatoes	Steamed green beans
Grilled chicken tenders	Corn	Grilled summer squash
Chicken drumstick	Brown rice	Steamed carrots and ginger

Other Tips

- Cook chicken to an internal temperature of 165°F and until juices run clear. To measure the temperature, insert a food thermometer into the center of the meat.
- Top chicken with healthy condiments for additional flavor and texture. Try spicy salsa, sweet grilled pineapple, crunchy chopped nuts, or creamy mustard.
- Prepare a whole chicken or several chicken breasts in the beginning of the week, and use in another recipe later that week. Leftover chicken makes a great addition to salads, stir-fry, and pasta dishes. Cooked chicken can be stored safely in the fridge for up to four days.

Turkey burger on whole grain sandwich thin, and grilled peppers and onions

Roast chicken wrapped in whole wheat tortilla, celery and carrot sticks, and Spicy Blue Cheese (page 115)

Filet with grilled onions and mushrooms, orzo, and steamed asparagus

BEEF

Healthy Preparation

The best method of preparation is truly dependent on the cut of meat. Tender cuts can be cooked quickly at higher temperatures over a grill or under a broiler. Tougher cuts become more tender when seared or browned and then cooked slowly with some liquid at lower temperatures (braising).

- **Grilling:** Tender cuts like loins and fillets fare well on the grill with a simple spice rub. Lean ground beef burgers are also great on the grill. Marinade flank steaks with spicy peppers, garlic, and lemon juice and grill until desired doneness. Serve leftover slices of flank steak on a salad.
- **Roasting:** Trim visible fat and rub roasts, such as eye round or sirloin tips, with garlic, thyme, and/or parsley and slow roast in the oven at a low temperature. Cut leftover meat into cubes and toss into soups, stews, or stir-fry dishes.

Sliced flank steak in whole wheat tortilla wrap, grilled peppers and onions, low-fat sour cream and guacamole

Lean meatballs, whole wheat spaghetti with Easy Tomato Sauce (pg 97) and grated parmesan, and green salad

SAUCE SUGGESTIONS	GREAT RUBS FOR BEEF	SIMPLE MARINADES
Top lean steaks with a splash of dry red wine and sautéed mushrooms	Rub steaks with cayenne pepper, cumin, and garlic and onion powders for some kick	Chipotle chilies, cilantro, and lime juice add some spice to flank steak
Low-fat creamy horseradish adds a kick to roast beef	Garlic and ground pepper make a simple rub for flavorful cuts, such as filet	A splash of sesame oil, reduced-sodium soy sauce, and grated ginger make a tasty Asian marinade

Suggested Pairings

The savory taste of beef pairs well with many vegetables and SmartCarbs. Below are some pairings to try.

POWERFUEL	SMARTCARB	VEGETABLE
Beef loin	Roasted sweet potatoes	Steamed asparagus
Beef tips	Brown rice	Mixed vegetables
Lean ground beef patty	Whole grain bun	Green salad

Other Tips

- When choosing cuts of beef, look for ones with the least amount of marbling, which is the visible fat. Trim excess fat before eating.
- Purchase lean ground beef or steaks when on sale and store in the freezer for up to six months.
- Marinating meats with a small amount of an acid, like vinegar or lemon juice, will help tenderize the meat.
- Be sure to measure the internal temperature of your meat to ensure it is safe to eat; refer to the Safe Minimum Cooking Temperatures Chart on page 155.

Roast beef with au jus and horseradish, whole grain roll, and steamed broccoli and cauliflower

Flank steak, black beans, and tomato and onion salad

Baked pork chop, chunky applesauce, and steamed green and wax beans

PORK

Healthy Preparation

Pork is a very versatile meat. While known for its bacon and sausage, many cuts are actually quite lean and can work well in a number of dishes. Be sure not to overcook leaner cuts, as they tend to dry out quickly.

- **Grilling:** Lean pork chops or pork loin work great on the grill. Rub the meat with sweet or savory spices before grilling.
- **Roasting:** Trim visible fat before placing the roast or pork loin in the oven at 325°F. Cook with sweet potatoes and chopped vegetables for a complete meal.
- **Braising:** Slow cooking pork is a tasty and convenient way to prepare larger, tougher cuts of pork like pork shoulder or roasts. Sear the meat over medium to high heat until lightly browned on all sides. Then place the meat in a slow cooker or in a covered pot over low to medium heat. Be sure to add some liquid, like water or reduced-sodium broth, and cook for several hours, until the pork reaches an internal temperature of 145°F. More acidic liquids, such as vinegar, can help tenderize the meat. This is a great way to prepare roasts or pulled pork.

Sliced pork, roasted sweet potatoes, and steamed snap peas sprinkled with almonds

Grilled pork chop, herbed couscous, and spinach salad

SAUCE SUGGESTIONS	GREAT RUBS FOR PORK	SIMPLE MARINADES
Top pork loin with sweet fruit compotes, such as cranberry or apricots	Rosemary and garlic work well on pork roast	Marinate a pork loin in reduced-sodium Asian sauces, such as teriyaki
Slow cook a lean roast or pork loin in barbeque sauce for an easy pulled pork dish	Rub boneless pork chops with a spicy jerk seasoning for some island flair	Dijon mustard, honey, and splash of white wine make an easy marinade for pork

Suggested Pairings

Pork also pairs well with sweet vegetables and SmartCarbs such as corn and sweet potato. Below are some suggested combinations.

POWERFUEL	SMARTCARB	VEGETABLE
Barbequed pulled pork	Whole grain bun	Coleslaw
Rosemary pork loin	Sweet potato	Steamed broccoli
Grilled pork chop	Corn on the cob	Tomato salad

Other Tips

- Trim visible fat before cooking a pork loin or roast to reduce fat and calorie content.
- Slow cook tougher cuts of pork to help tenderize them and enhance flavor.
- Slice leftover pork loin and use as a salad topper or dice it up and add it to an Asian stir-fry.
- Cook pork to an internal temperature of 145°F, but let the meat rest for three minutes after it reaches this temperature. Refer to the Safe Minimum Cooking Temperatures Chart on page 155.

Barbeque pulled pork in whole wheat pita, and vegetable slaw

Boneless, honey-glazed pork chop, brown rice, and steamed Brussels sprouts and carrots

Broiled salmon, whole grain dinner roll, and mixed green salad

FISH AND SHELLFISH

Healthy Preparation

Most fish and shellfish are low in fat and calories and offer a great source of protein. Some varieties of fish offer omega-3 fatty acids, which have been shown to promote heart health. Fish and shellfish can be cooked in a variety of ways and complement a variety of dishes, from grilled kabobs to pasta. They are easy to purchase, prepare, and even store.

- **Grilling:** Sturdy, fattier fish such as salmon, tuna, and swordfish do best on the grill. Lean fish and shellfish will cook quickly over the high heat of the grill. (Be sure not to overcook!) Layer shrimp and scallops with fresh vegetables marinated in lemon juice and fresh herbs for a quick dinner.
- **Broiling:** Rub fish and shellfish with spices and place under broiler for just a few minutes. Flip thicker fillets over midway through cooking. Broiling helps create a crunchy "crust" on the fish, without adding extra fat and calories.

Grilled shrimp kabobs, couscous, and grilled summer squash

Broiled flounder, brown rice, and steamed broccoli and carrots

SAUCE SUGGESTIONS	GREAT RUBS FOR FISH	SIMPLE MARINADES
Top tilapia with a southwestern salsa	Fresh dill and lemon zest complement salmon	Marinate shellfish in lemon juice and garlic for a simple, tasty dish
Dip steamed shrimp into a low-fat cocktail sauce	Rub catfish with a zesty Creole spice mix	Dijon mustard and a splash of white wine make an easy marinade for fish

Suggested Pairings

Fish and shellfish work best with lighter fare. Try the following SmartCarb and Vegetable combinations.

POWERFUEL	SMARTCARB	VEGETABLE
Broiled salmon	Whole grain roll	Green salad
Seared scallops	Whole wheat linguine	Steamed asparagus
Stir-fried shrimp	Brown rice	Mixed vegetables

Other Tips

- Fish and shellfish are lean sources of protein. Try them as a substitute for meats in tacos, on salads, or in pasta dishes.
- Cold water fish, such as salmon and tuna, offer a good source of heart-healthy omega-3 fatty acids. Enjoy at least two servings of fish per week, in accordance with recommendations from the American Heart Association.
- Avoid purchasing any fish that give off a fishy odor. This may indicate this particular fish or cut is past its prime.
- Purchase fish that were wild-caught or farm-raised in sustainable fisheries.
- Thaw frozen fish in the refrigerator or under cold running water.
- Fish flesh is already tender and more susceptible to acidic marinades. So marinate fish for no more than an hour or two.
- Cook fish and shellfish until opaque. Fish will flake easily when fully cooked.

Seared scallops, whole wheat angel hair pasta, and sautéed spinach

Breaded tilapia, chickpea salad, and steamed green beans sprinkled with slivered almonds

Grilled tofu triangles, brown rice, and grilled vegetables

VEGETARIAN OPTIONS

Healthy Preparation

Vegetarian meals can be as tasty and satisfying as dishes made with meat, and many meat-eaters are choosing vegetarian dishes more often. This section will include dishes that provide a complete source of protein—those that contain all of the essential amino acids—and may include protein from milk and egg sources. Animal protein sources (meats, eggs, milk, and cheese) offer all essential amino acids, but vegetarians should eat a **variety** of nonmeat protein sources to ensure they obtain all essential amino acids in their diet. Good sources of vegetarian protein include:

- Beans
- Soy products
- Nuts
- Nut butters
- Dairy
- Eggs

Polenta topped with Easy Tomato Sauce (Pg 97) and low-fat cheese, and sautéed spinach and mushrooms

Roasted vegetables in a whole wheat tortilla, low-fat cheese, and hummus

Suggested Pairings

POWERFUEL	SMARTCARB	VEGETABLE	EXTRA
Egg frittata	Whole wheat toast	Broccoli	1 teaspoon margarine
Tofu	Brown rice	Mixed vegetables	1 teaspoon Asian sauce or marinade
Low-fat cheese	Kidney beans	Green salad	1 tablespoon low-fat dressing
Pine nuts	Whole grain pasta	Sautéed spinach	1 teaspoon Parmesan cheese

Other Alternative Vegetarian Proteins

Tempeh is a soy-derived alternative vegetarian protein. Although tempeh and tofu both come from soybean, tempeh differs from tofu in texture and flavor. Tempeh offers a nutty flavor and a more chewy texture. Purchase frozen tempeh and add to stir-fry dishes, soup, and sauces, or marinate and cook as you choose. Two ounces of tempeh is equivalent to one PowerFuel.

Seitan is a gluten or wheat-based vegetarian option that resembles meat. Seitan can be cooked in many different ways but is best marinated and seared. Purchase seitan frozen or refrigerated. Four ounces of seitan is equivalent to one PowerFuel.

Other ready-to-go vegetarian convenience foods, such as soy dogs, bean burgers, and vegetable patties, can also make great meat alternatives. Just be cautious of the sodium content.

Tofu cubes, whole wheat noodles, stir-fried vegetables, and red curry sauce

Portobello "burger" with low-fat cheese on whole wheat sandwich thin, and green salad with hard-boiled egg

Fresh mozzarella, chick pea, and tomato salad with reduced fat balsamic vinaigrette dressing

SALADS

Healthy Preparation

Mix and match ingredients to create a variety of simple, healthful dinner salads. Choose from a variety of salad greens for your base, leftover meats to provide PowerFuels, and canned beans to provide SmartCarbs. Or visit your supermarket salad bar if you are on the go.

Keep in mind, salads toppings can be a hidden source of fat and calories. So use lean meats and lower-fat cheeses, and always be mindful of portion sizes. The amounts of added nuts, seeds, and dressings should be limited, as their calories can quickly add up.

Other Tips

- Purchase prewashed, bagged salad leaves for convenience.
- Use leftover or reduced-sodium canned chicken or salmon as a quick, easy, and protein-packed salad topper.
- Chopped nuts add a fun crunch, as well as heart-healthy fats, to salads.

Arugula salad, roast chicken, chopped walnuts, sliced apples, and reduced-fat raspberry vinaigrette dressing

Chef salad with lettuce, tomatoes, lean ham, hard-boiled egg, reduced-fat ranch dressing, and whole grain roll

Suggested Pairings

POWERFUEL	SMARTCARB	VEGETABLE	EXTRA
Roasted chicken	Strawberries	Baby spinach	Fat-free berry vinaigrette
Fat-free feta cheese	Chick peas	Romaine lettuce with tomatoes and cucumbers	Low-fat Greek dressing
Salmon	Whole grain roll	Mixed greens	Low-fat balsamic vinaigrette
Low-fat mozzarella cheese	White beans	Grilled or roasted summer vegetables	Fat-free Italian dressing
Broiled shrimp	Whole wheat orzo	Baby arugula	Low-fat vinaigrette

- Canned beans make a healthy, fiber-rich salad topper. Look for reduced-sodium varieties.
- When possible, purchase local produce from a nearby farmers' market. You may save money and get fresher salad ingredients.
- Topping your salad with a rainbow of colorful vegetables will ensure you get a variety of important nutrients and phytochemicals.

Romaine salad with roast chicken, tomatoes, reduced-fat Caesar dressing, and whole grain dinner roll

Spinach salad, shrimp, mandarin oranges, sliced almonds, and reduced-fat sesame vinaigrette dressing

NUTRISYSTEM-

Nutrisystem has taken great care in selecting and developing recipes that meet our nutrition standards and the specific nutritional requirements of our program. The included recipes provide lean proteins, heart-healthy fats, and high-fiber, low GI sources of carbohydrates. This balance not only provides good nutrition, but leaves you feeling satisfied and helps you stay on track with your weight management goals. With simple ingredients and preparation methods, the recipes are great for every day but delicious enough to serve on special occasions!

Many of these recipes were developed and tested by the Nutrisystem Research and Development Team with Max Sugarman in the Nutrisystem test kitchen, and tasted by a panel of food and product development experts. In partnership with the expert authors of the *New Glucose Revolution,* Nutrisystem has adapted several other recipes from the *Low GI Family Cookbook* and *The New Glucose Revolution Life Plan* to fit the portion size specifications of this cookbook. The New Glucose Revolution Team has years of scientific and culinary expertise in developing and promoting low GI cooking. Their recipes produce simply delicious results and offer healthy basics as well as more sophisticated dishes.

All recipes were analyzed using the Genesis® R&D SQL v9.6.0.0 from ESHA Research, Salem, OR. The nutritional information per serving of each recipe is provided. Halve or double recipes as needed. Many of the recipes can be made ahead and stored in the freezer.

APPROVED recipes

USING THE RECIPES

Recipes are organized by meal occasion: Breakfast, Lunches and Soups, Starters and Snacks, Dinner, and Dessert. Each recipe provides a Nutrisystem® Program equivalent per serving. This way, you can equate the recipe serving to a Nutrisystem® meal occasion and/or add-in food, such as a SmartCarb, a PowerFuel, or an Optional Extra. For example, one serving of the Sweet Apple Turkey Burgers on page 119 counts as a Nutrisystem® Dinner. If you enjoy it with a half cup of baked sweet potato fries and a cup of vegetable slaw as suggested, you would also count a SmartCarb and Vegetable on your daily tracker.

Important note: It is OK to move an add-in from another meal occasion—as long as you remember to only eat that particular add-in once. For example, you could move your SmartCarb from dinner to lunch, which means you will enjoy your Nutrisystem Dinner occasion with one less SmartCarb. Keep in mind that you can always add more nonstarchy Vegetables, which are unlimited.

> With Nutrisystem, I gained an understanding of proper nutrition; I learned how to eat smart.
>
> —JOHN N.

RECIPE TABLE OF CONTENTS

Breakfast

Lunches and Soups

Starters and Snacks

Dinner

Dessert

BREAKFAST
recipes

Breakfast truly is the most important meal of the day. Studies have suggested that people who skip breakfast may be missing out on important nutrients and may have more difficulty maintaining a healthy weight. Starting your day with a balance of SmartCarbs, in the form of whole grains and fruits, and PowerFuels, in the form of eggs, lean meats, and nuts, helps ensure you have the sustainable energy you need to get through your morning. These recipes include simple recipes you can throw together on weekday mornings and more sophisticated dishes for weekends and special occasions.

◀ Mixed Berry Parfait with Graham Crackers and Walnuts, page 40

Mixed Berry Parfait with Graham Crackers and Walnuts SERVES 2

Berries provide health-enhancing antioxidants while walnuts provide heart-healthy fats. Use other fruit and nut combinations to create parfait varieties, such as bananas and walnuts, or pears and almonds.

PREP TIME 5 minutes

INGREDIENTS

3 squares reduced-fat graham crackers, crushed

2 tablespoons roasted walnuts, chopped

1 cup low-fat plain or vanilla yogurt

¾ cup fresh or frozen blueberries, thawed

½ cup fresh or frozen raspberries, thawed

METHOD

1 Mix the graham crackers and chopped walnuts together in a small mixing bowl.

2 Spoon one-quarter of the nut and graham cracker mixture into two small glasses.

3 Layer ½ cup yogurt and ¾ cup fruit into each glass.

4 Top each parfait with remaining chopped walnut and graham cracker mixture, split evenly between the glasses.

COOKING TIP To roast walnuts, preheat oven to 350°F and place walnuts on small oven pan and bake for about 10 minutes until nuts are lightly browned.

PER SERVING (1 parfait)

200 calories
7 g fat
1 g saturated fat
8 g protein
28 g carbohydrate
2 g fiber
11 g sugar
110 mg sodium

NUTRISYSTEM EQUIVALENT

Nutrisystem® Breakfast Entrée

Breakfast Smoothie SERVES 2

Smoothies can be an easy, on-the-go breakfast that offers protein, fiber, and plenty of vitamins and minerals. The wheat germ adds iron, zinc, and fiber and can usually be found in your grocer's baking aisle.

PREP TIME 5 minutes

INGREDIENTS

½ cup low-fat or nonfat milk

½ cup low-fat, reduced-sugar yogurt

1 cup fresh or frozen strawberries, tops removed

2 teaspoons wheat germ

1 teaspoon honey

METHOD

1 Combine all ingredients in a blender.

2 Blend and serve!

> **SERVING TIP** Try other smoothie combinations such as banana and almond milk or peaches and soy milk.

PER SERVING
(approximately ¾ cup)

    120 calories
    2 g fat
    1 g saturated fat
    6 g protein
    21 g carbohydrate
    3 g fiber
    16 g sugar
    45 mg sodium

NUTRISYSTEM EQUIVALENT

Nutrisystem® Breakfast Entrée

Almost immediately, eating healthier became a habit
and changed the way I cook for my whole family.
So now we're all living better together!

—DEBRA M.

Morning Salmon Salad SERVES 2

Salmon is a great source of heart-healthy omega-3 fatty acids and is a rich source of protein. Use leftover cooked salmon or canned salmon if you don't have fresh fish on hand.

PREP TIME 5 to 10 minutes

INGREDIENTS

3 ounces cooked salmon fillet

2 tablespoons reduced-fat cream cheese

2 slices whole grain bread, toasted

2 teaspoons chives, chopped (optional)

Black pepper, to taste

METHOD

1 Shred salmon with a fork.

2 Mix the cream cheese and salmon.

3 When cream cheese and salmon are mixed, add the chives and season with black pepper to taste.

4 Divide salmon salad evenly, and spread on toast slices.

PER SERVING (1 slice toast topped with ½ salmon salad spread)

150 calories
4.5 g fat
1.5 g saturated fat
14 g protein
15 g carbohydrate
5 g fiber
2 g sugar
190 mg sodium

NUTRISYSTEM EQUIVALENT

Nutrisystem® Breakfast Entrée

Eggs in Nest SERVES 2

This recipe makes a great weekend breakfast or brunch dish, and is a fun way to sneak vegetables into your morning meal. Eggs are an iron-rich source of protein, and the whole grain toast offers filling fiber. Experiment with different vegetables for variety.

PREP TIME 10 minutes   COOKING TIME 15 to 20 minutes

INGREDIENTS

2 slices of whole grain bread

Cooking spray, as needed

5 button mushrooms, sliced

3 large spinach leaves, sliced

Black pepper, to taste

2 whole eggs

1 tablespoon low-fat cheddar cheese, shredded

METHOD

1 Preheat oven to 350°F.

2 Cut crusts off the bread. Spray both sides of each slice lightly with oil. Press the bread slices firmly into two nonstick muffin pan holes. Set aside.

3 Spray pan lightly with cooking spray and place over medium heat. Add the mushrooms and cook, stirring often, for 4 to 5 minutes or until tender. Add the spinach and cook, stirring, for 1 to 2 minutes or until wilted. Remove from heat and season with pepper.

4 Divide mushroom mixture between the bread cases. Crack an egg into a small dish and then slide it into one of the bread cases. Repeat with the remaining egg. Sprinkle with the cheese. Bake for 15 minutes (for a softly set yolk), 20 minutes (for a hard-cooked yolk), or until the egg is cooked to your liking. Serve warm or at room temperature.

PER SERVING (1 egg nest)

190 calories
6 g fat
2 g saturated fat
14 g protein
20 g carbohydrate
4 g fiber
3 g sugar
280 mg sodium

NUTRISYSTEM EQUIVALENT

Nutrisystem® Breakfast Entrée

> **SERVING TIP** This recipe is fun for kids to help prepare and eat.

French Toast with Strawberry and Banana Topping SERVES 2

A sweet breakfast without the guilt! Strawberries and bananas add fiber, vitamin C, and some sweetness, but sugar-free syrup can also be added.

PREP TIME 5 minutes COOKING TIME 5 minutes

INGREDIENTS

Strawberry and Banana Topping

½ cup strawberries, tops removed and halved

½ banana, sliced

2 teaspoons sugar-free maple syrup

French Toast

1 egg

1 tablespoon low-fat milk

½ teaspoon vanilla extract

1 teaspoon olive or canola oil margarine

2 thick slices whole grain bread, halved

METHOD

1 To make the Strawberry and Banana Topping, combine all the ingredients in a small bowl.

2 To make the French Toast, use a fork to whisk together the egg, milk, and vanilla in a shallow bowl.

3 Heat a large nonstick frying pan over medium heat. Rub the margarine over the base of the pan. Dip the bread slices in the egg mixture, allowing the bread to soak it up. Remove the bread, allowing any excess egg mixture to drain off. When the margarine is sizzling, add the dipped bread to the pan and cook for 2 minutes each side or until well browned. Top with fruit and serve immediately.

SERVING TIP For variety, top French Toast with fresh peaches, pears, or blueberries.

NUTRITION TIP Look for 100% whole grain breads with lots of grainy texture, as they tend to offer a lower GI.

PER SERVING (1 slice toast with ½ cup fruit and 1 teaspoon syrup)

170 calories
5 g fat
1 g saturated fat
6 g protein
28 g carbohydrate
7 g fiber
8 g sugar
115 mg sodium

NUTRISYSTEM EQUIVALENT

Nutrisystem® Breakfast Entrée

Banana Oatmeal with Toasted Walnuts SERVES 2

Fire up your engine for the day with nourishing, satisfying oatmeal. The banana provides some sweetness, and the oats offer soluble fiber, which has been shown to help reduce cholesterol.

PREP TIME 5 minutes   COOKING TIME 10 minutes

INGREDIENTS

½ cup rolled oats

¼ cup cold water

1 cup boiling water

1 small banana

1½ tablespoons toasted walnuts

1 tablespoon low-fat milk (optional)

½ teaspoon sugar substitute, or to taste (optional)

METHOD

1 Combine the rolled oats and cold water in a small saucepan. Add the boiling water and banana and stir well to combine.

2 Bring the oatmeal to a boil over medium heat, stirring often. Reduce the heat and simmer, stirring often, for 5 minutes or until thick and creamy, adding a little more water if necessary to reach desired consistency.

3 Add sugar substitute if desired. Spoon ½ cup oatmeal in each bowl and top each serving with ¾ tablespoon toasted walnuts. Serve immediately.

> **SERVING TIP** Add 1 teaspoon of honey (1 Extra) to your oatmeal for some additional sweetness.

PER SERVING (½ cup)

170 calories
5 g fat
0.5 g saturated fat
4 g protein
27 g carbohydrate
4 g fiber
5 g sugar
0 mg sodium

NUTRISYSTEM EQUIVALENT

Nutrisystem® Breakfast Entrée

Black Bean and Rice Breakfast Scramble SERVES 2

This quick breakfast offers lean protein from the egg and fiber from the beans to help fill you up. Wrap it in a whole wheat tortilla and make a tasty breakfast burrito for those days when you're on the go!

PREP TIME 10 minutes   **COOKING TIME** 5 minutes

INGREDIENTS

Cooking spray, as needed

3 large egg whites or ¼ cup egg substitute

⅓ cup canned black beans, rinsed

⅓ cup cooked brown rice

½ ounce reduced-fat pepper jack cheese

1 small roma tomato, diced

½ tablespoon fresh cilantro, chopped (optional)

Black pepper, to taste

6-inch whole wheat tortilla wraps, optional (SmartCarb)

METHOD

1 Lightly coat a nonstick frying pan with cooking spray and place on stove top over medium heat.

2 Add egg whites to frying pan.

3 Cook eggs for 1 to 2 minutes. Then add the black beans, cooked rice, cheese, diced tomatoes, and cilantro.

4 Scramble mixture until eggs are completely cooked.

5 Add half the mixture to soft tortilla shell (SmartCarb) for a tasty breakfast burrito, if desired.

SERVING TIP Add a cup of spinach, peppers, zucchini, or other nonstarchy vegetables to this dish. Or spice it up with 1 tablespoon of salsa or dash of hot sauce as desired (Extra).

NUTRITION TIP Beans are a great low GI food that offer a delicious source of iron, calcium, and B vitamins.

PER SERVING (½ recipe)

120 calories
2.5 g fat
1.5 g saturated fat
10 g protein
15 g carbohydrate
3 g fiber
2 g sugar
220 mg sodium

NUTRISYSTEM EQUIVALENT

Nutrisystem® Breakfast Entrée

Nutrisystem helps you discover ways of getting what
you want and what you need, so that you can continue to
live healthier well after you reach your goal.

—MICHELLE R.

Steak & Cheese Omelet with Whole Wheat Toast SERVES 2

A great breakfast for steak lovers! This protein-packed omelet is filled with savory onions, mushrooms, and mozzarella cheese. Serve with a slice of whole grain bread for a complete meal.

PREP TIME 10 minutes   COOKING TIME 10 minutes

INGREDIENTS

Cooking spray, as needed

⅓ cup onion, diced

⅓ cup mushrooms, diced

2 ounces lean steak, such as flank steak (sliced thin)

3 egg whites

1 tablespoon low-fat milk

½ ounce reduced-sodium mozzarella cheese or ¼ cup

Black pepper, to taste

2 slices whole grain toast, to serve

METHOD

1 Lightly coat a medium-size frying pan with cooking spray.

2 Over medium to high heat, sauté onions and mushrooms for about 3 minutes, until onions start to brown.

3 Add steak and continue cooking until steak is fully cooked, about an additional 2 to 3 minutes.

4 Remove steak and sautéed vegetables and set aside.

5 Whisk egg whites with low-fat milk in small bowl.

6 Lightly coat a nonstick omelet pan (about 8 inches in diameter) with cooking spray and place over low to medium heat.

7 Add all of the egg and milk mixture. When egg mixture starts to cook, about 1 to 2 minutes, spread steak and sautéed vegetables over egg and top with mozzarella cheese.

8 When egg is firm and cooked through, fold omelet in half.

9 Cut omelet into two equal servings. Serve ½ the omelet with one slice of whole grain toast.

PER SERVING (½ omelet and 1 slice toast)

170 calories
4 g fat
1.5 g saturated fat
18 g protein
16 g carbohydrate
2 g fiber
4 g sugar
240 mg sodium

NUTRISYSTEM EQUIVALENT

Nutrisystem® Breakfast Entrée

Yogurt and Strawberry Filled Crepes SERVES 6

Crepes may seem complicated, but this easy recipe will have you impressing family and friends. Fill crepes with good-for-you fillings like fruits and PowerFuels such as yogurt, soft cheeses, or nut butters—the possibilities are endless!

PREP TIME 10 minutes **COOKING TIME** 10 to 15 minutes

INGREDIENTS

½ cup egg substitute or
   2 whole eggs

½ cup whole wheat flour

1 cup all-purpose flour

1½ cups nonfat milk

1 teaspoon vanilla extract

¾ cup low-fat vanilla yogurt

1½ cups chopped strawberries

Cooking spray, as needed

METHOD

1 In a large bowl, whisk together eggs and flour. Gradually add in milk and vanilla, stirring to combine.

2 Lightly coat a 6- to 7-inch nonstick pan with cooking spray and place over medium heat.

3 Using a measuring cup, pour a thin layer of batter into the pan (about 3 tablespoons of batter per crepe). Tilt the pan until the batter coats the bottom surface evenly.

4 Cook the crepe for about 30 seconds, until the bottom is lightly browned. Using a rubber spatula, flip crepe and cook for another 30 seconds.

5 Repeat until you have used all of the remaining batter. Recipe yields about 12 crepes.

6 Fill each crepe with 1 tablespoon of yogurt and 2 tablespoons of strawberries. Roll and enjoy.

PER SERVING (2 crepes)

160 calories
0.5 g fat
0 g saturated fat
9 g protein
30 g carbohydrate
2 g fiber
7 g sugar
80 mg sodium

NUTRISYSTEM EQUIVALENT

Nutrisystem® Breakfast Entrée

COOKING TIP For a sweeter crepe, add sugar substitute to the batter prior to cooking.

Rocky Mountain Toast
with Avocado and Tomato Salsa SERVES 2

A tasty version of the classic breakfast sandwich. Avocado adds a creamy texture, as well as heart-healthy fats.

PREP TIME Less than 10 minutes   COOKING TIME Less than 10 minutes

INGREDIENTS

1 small tomato, diced

¼ of whole avocado, peeled and diced

1 teaspoon white wine vinegar

Black pepper, to taste

2 slices whole grain bread

Cooking spray

2 eggs

METHOD

Avocado and Tomato Salsa

1 Mix diced tomato and avocado together in small bowl.

2 Add white wine vinegar and season with black pepper to taste.

Rocky Mountain Toast

1 Tear a 2½- to 3-inch circle hole into the center of each slice of bread.

2 Lightly coat a skillet or a large nonstick pan with cooking spray and place over medium-high heat.

3 Crack an egg in the hole of each slice of bread.

4 Heat the bread until it's golden brown and the egg is cooked, then flip bread and repeat on the other side. Cook for about 2 minutes on each side.

5 Top each slice of Rocky Mountain Toast with the avocado and tomato salsa, and serve.

PER SERVING (1 slice of bread, with 1 egg, and ½ salsa mixture)

180 calories
9 g fat
2 g saturated fat
10 g protein
15 g carbohydrate
4 g fiber
3 g sugar
170 mg sodium

NUTRISYSTEM EQUIVALENT

Nutrisystem® Breakfast Entrée

NUTRITION TIP If you are concerned about cholesterol, consider limiting your intake of egg yolks to two per week.

SERVING TIP If desired, top toast with 1 slice low-fat cheese (PowerFuel).

Mix-It-Up Granola SERVES 2

This wholesome cereal provides the perfect balance of SmartCarbs (oats and dried fruits) and PowerFuels (nuts). Use it as a topping for yogurt or serve with a cup of nonfat milk.

PREP TIME 5 minutes   **COOKING TIME** 20 to 30 minutes

INGREDIENTS

⅓ cup rolled oats

2 teaspoons vegetable oil

1 teaspoon honey

2 tablespoons reduced-calorie maple syrup

CHOOSE YOUR ADDITIONAL INGREDIENTS

1 POWERFUEL	1 SMARTCARB	EXTRA (optional)
2 tablespoons of raw nuts: almonds, hazelnuts, walnuts, peanuts, cashews, or pistachios	½ cup dried fruit: raisins, cranberries, banana chips, cherries, apricots, figs, or pineapple	cinnamon or nutmeg

METHOD

1 Preheat oven to 300°F.

2 In small bowl, mix rolled oats, nuts, honey, maple syrup, and oil.

3 Spread oat mixture on a small sheet pan and bake until golden brown, approximately 20 to 30 minutes, stirring every 10 minutes.

4 Let granola cool, then mix in dried fruit.

COOKING TIP This cereal can be made ahead in larger quantities and stored in an airtight container at room temperature for about a week.

PER SERVING
(approximately ½ cup)

240 Calories
10 g fat
1 g saturated fat
5 g protein
34 g carbohydrate
4 g fiber
18 g sugar
45 mg sodium

NUTRISYSTEM EQUIVALENT

Nutrisystem® Breakfast Entrée + 2 Extras

Banana Bread 10 SLICES

This banana bread is a sweet breakfast treat that can conveniently be made ahead of time. Double this recipe and freeze individual slices for a grab and go breakfast. Making the bread with whole wheat flour adds filling fiber and more vitamins and minerals.

PREP TIME 20 minutes   COOKING TIME 50 to 55 minutes

INGREDIENTS

Cooking spray

7 tablespoons olive oil margarine

¾ cup firmly packed brown sugar

2 eggs

2 small ripe bananas

⅓ cup buttermilk

¾ cup all-purpose flour

½ cup whole wheat flour

1½ teaspoons baking soda

1½ teaspoons ground cinnamon

½ cup unprocessed oat bran

PER SERVING (1 slice)

250 calories
12 g fat
2 g saturated fat
4 g protein
36 g carbohydrate
2 g fiber
19 g sugar
330 mg sodium

NUTRISYSTEM EQUIVALENT

Nutrisystem® Breakfast Entrée +
1 SmartCarb

METHOD

1 Preheat oven to 350°F. Lightly spray a medium loaf pan (8 x 4 inches) with oil and line the base and the two long sides with a piece of nonstick baking paper.

2 Combine the margarine and sugar in a large mixing bowl and beat with an electric mixer until light and creamy.

3 Add the eggs one at a time, beating well after each addition, until the mixture is pale and fluffy.

4 Mash the bananas and stir into the mixture with the buttermilk using a large metal spoon to combine well.

5 Sift the flour, baking soda, and cinnamon together into a mixing bowl, add the oat bran, and stir to combine. Add to the banana mixture and fold in until just combined.

6 Spoon into the prepared loaf pan and smooth the surface with the back of a spoon. Bake the banana bread for 50 to 55 minutes or until a toothpick inserted into the center comes out clean. Stand in the pan for 5 minutes before turning onto a wire rack to cool.

7 After banana bread is cooled and removed from pan, slice bread into ten evenly sized pieces. Store bread in an airtight container in a cool place unrefrigerated for up to four days.

COOKING TIP Use parchment paper for best results. If parchment paper is not available, use cooking spray to coat loaf pan.

AND SOUPS recipes

Eating a healthful, well-balanced lunch can be the secret to staving off that potentially sabotaging afternoon hunger. Choose lean meats, fiber-rich beans and legumes, whole grains, fruit, and filling vegetables. Veggies are an especially important hunger management tool, as they are low in calories but high in water and fiber content, which fill you up. So be sure to pack in a serving or two with each lunch meal. Many of the lunch recipes in this book can be made ahead and reheat well. Make an effort to plan a few meals each week.

◄ Bruschetta, page 60

Bruschetta SERVES 2

Bruschetta makes an easy and fun appetizer to serve at or bring to your next gathering, and it's great for lunch. We've provided three combinations to inspire you, but try your own variations with fresh vegetables and low-fat cheeses. Sourdough bread is lower on the glycemic index.

PREP TIME 15 minutes   **COOKING TIME** 10 minutes

INGREDIENTS

Sourdough baguette

Pureed avocado topped with smoked salmon bruschetta

¼ of whole avocado, peeled

1 tablespoon reduced-fat sour cream

1 teaspoon lime juice

Black pepper to taste

2 slices smoked salmon (lox)

Cordon bleu bruschetta

2 tablespoons reduced-fat shredded mozzarella

2 slices reduced-sodium deli ham

Lime, tomato, and basil bruschetta

1 small tomato, seeds removed and diced

1 teaspoon lime juice

1 tablespoon onion, chopped

1 tablespoon basil, chopped

PER SERVING (3 slices bruschetta, 1 of each style)

   240 calories
   6 g fat
   1.5 g saturated fat
   11 g protein
   33 g carbohydrate
   4 g fiber
   2 g sugar
   430 mg sodium

METHOD

Baguettes

1 Preheat oven to 350°F.

2 Slice baguette into six ½-inch pieces.

3 Toast baguette slices in oven or toaster until crispy and set aside until toppings are ready.

Pureed avocado topped with smoked salmon bruschetta

1 Mash avocado with a fork.

2 Combine mashed avocado, sour cream, and lime juice. Add black pepper as desired.

3 Spread the avocado mixture evenly on two toasted baguette slices, top with the smoked salmon and serve.

Cordon bleu bruschetta

1 Top two toasted baguette slices with ½ teaspoon mozzarella each.

2 Place one slice of ham on top of the mozzarella, then top with the remaining tablespoon of cheese, spilt between the two baguettes.

3 Heat in oven for 3 minutes or until cheese is melted.

Lime tomato and basil bruschetta

1 Combine diced tomatoes, lime juice, diced onion, and basil in small bowl.

2 Top the two toasted baguette slices evenly with tomato mixture. Serve.

NUTRISYSTEM EQUIVALENT   Nutrisystem® Lunch Entrée

Creamy Broccoli Soup SERVES 4

This soup is packed with nutrient-rich broccoli and has a wonderful creamy consistency the whole family will enjoy. For added convenience, make ahead and reheat in the microwave.

PREP TIME 15 minutes   COOKING TIME 35 minutes

INGREDIENTS

1 tablespoon olive oil

1 medium onion, diced

9 cups fresh or frozen broccoli florets, chopped (about 4 heads of broccoli)

5 cloves of garlic, minced

2 cups low-fat milk

1½ cups reduced-sodium chicken broth or vegetable broth

3 tablespoons all-purpose flour

Black pepper, to taste

4 tablespoons reduced-sodium shredded cheddar cheese

4 slices whole grain bread or small rolls

METHOD

1 Add oil to a medium pot and place over low to medium heat.

2 When oil is heated, add diced onions and broccoli, and cook for 10 minutes, until vegetables start to soften, stirring occasionally.

3 Add the minced garlic and continue cooking for another 3 minutes, being careful not to burn the garlic.

4 Add the flour, and mix until the vegetables are caked with flour.

5 Add milk and chicken broth, and turn up heat slightly until the liquid starts to boil. Once boiling, reduce heat to a slow simmer.

6 Simmer for 10 to 15 minutes, until liquid begins to thicken.

7 Remove soup from the heat and allow to cool slightly (about 5 minutes).

8 Strain broccoli and onions and save soup broth. While straining, catch and reserve the soup broth with another pot or large bowl.

9 Combine strained broccoli and onions in a blender with 1½ cups soup broth and puree until smooth. Adjust the consistency of the soup by adding more broth to the blender as desired. Season to taste with black pepper if desired.

10 Sprinkle 1 cup of soup with 1 tablespoon of shredded cheddar cheese and serve hot with slice of whole grain bread or small roll.

PER SERVING (1 cup soup and 1 slice bread)

260 calories
8 g fat
3 g saturated fat
15 g protein
38 g carbohydrate
11 g fiber
10 g sugar
430 mg sodium

NUTRISYSTEM EQUIVALENT

Nutrisystem® Lunch Entrée

NUTRITION TIP Frozen vegetables may offer as many nutrients as fresh, since they are often frozen soon after they are picked.

Butternut Squash and Almond Soup SERVES 4

This velvety soup features flavors from autumn spices, such as nutmeg and cinnamon. The butternut squash adds the rich orange color and is an excellent source of vitamins A and C.

PREP TIME 15 minutes   COOKING TIME 20 to 25 minutes

INGREDIENTS

5 cups diced butternut squash, peeled and seeds removed

1 small onion, diced

3 cups reduced-sodium vegetable stock

2 cups almond milk, plain or vanilla

1 teaspoon ground nutmeg

1 teaspoon ground cinnamon

½ teaspoon salt or salt substitute

Black pepper, to taste

½ cup roasted almonds, sliced

METHOD

1 Place all ingredients, except sliced almonds, salt, and pepper, in a medium to large pot.

2 Bring soup to a boil and then reduce to a slow simmer.

3 Simmer soup until squash is tender and easily pierced with a fork, about 15 minutes.

4 Remove soup from heat and allow to cool for 5 minutes.

5 Strain squash and onions, and save soup broth. While straining, catch and reserve the soup broth with another pot or large bowl.

6 Combine butternut squash, onions, 1½ cups of the strained broth, and salt and pepper and blend until smooth. Check the consistency and flavor, and add more broth or spices if desired.

7 Spoon into bowls, and top soup with 2 tablespoons roasted almonds to serve.

PER SERVING (1 cup soup topped with 2 tablespoons almonds)

170 calories
7 g fat
.5 g saturated fat
5 g protein
27 g carbohydrate
6 g fiber
5 g sugar
360 mg sodium

NUTRISYSTEM EQUIVALENT

Nutrisystem® Lunch Entrée

> **COOKING TIP** Butternut squash can be difficult to cut. If using a whole squash, pierce the squash with a sharp knife twice on each side, then microwave on high for about 3 minutes. Squash will be easier to peel and cut.

Shrimp with Sweet Pineapple Rice SERVES 4

Shrimp are a great source of lean protein and pair well with sweet pineapple. Basmati rice, a long-grain rice known for its fragrance, is typically grown in India but can be found with other rice or in the ethnic food aisle of your local grocery store.

PREP TIME 15 minutes   COOKING TIME 45 minutes

INGREDIENTS

2 teaspoons vegetable oil

1 small red or green bell pepper, diced

1 small onion, diced

¾ cup basmati rice, uncooked

1¾ cups reduced-sodium chicken broth or water

One 8-ounce can chopped pineapple in 100% juice, drained

1 tablespoon reduced-sodium soy sauce

8 ounces cooked shrimp, fresh or frozen, thawed

METHOD

1 In a medium pot, heat oil over medium to high heat.

2 Once oil is heated, reduce heat to low and sauté the peppers and onions for about 5 minutes, stirring occasionally.

3 While the vegetables are sautéing, rinse the basmati rice in a strainer until water runs clear, about 2 minutes.

4 Add the rice to the pot with the vegetables, stirring to coat the rice with oil. This will help prevent the rice from sticking to the pot.

5 Add the chicken broth, pineapple, and soy sauce to the pot.

6 Bring rice to a boil, then reduce to a slow simmer and cover saucepan with a lid. Let simmer for about 15 to 20 minutes or until rice is soft.

7 Turn off heat and add the cooked shrimp to pot to reheat, for about 5 minutes. Fluff rice with a spoon or fork and serve.

PER SERVING (1 cup)

210 calories
3.5 g fat
0 g saturated fat
17 g protein
27 g carbohydrate
1 g fiber
10 g sugar
290 mg sodium

NUTRISYSTEM EQUIVALENT

Nutrisystem® Lunch Entrée

COOKING TIP If using raw shrimp, cook the shrimp in slow boiling water for about 3 minutes until pink. Shrimp cooks quickly, so be sure not to overcook.

Spinach Salad with Strawberry and Mint Yogurt Dressing SERVES 2

This salad is rich in antioxidants and is simple enough to take to work but tasty enough to serve guests.

PREP TIME 10 minutes

INGREDIENTS

2 cups fresh strawberries, sliced

1½ teaspoons fresh mint, chopped

1 teaspoon honey

3 ounces plain, low-fat yogurt

Sugar substitute, to taste

5 cups baby spinach

1½ tablespoons sunflower seeds

2 tablespoons feta cheese

METHOD

Dressing

1 Combine ¾ cup of strawberries, mint, honey, and yogurt in a blender.

2 Blend until smooth, adding sugar substitute to taste.

Salad

1 Slice the remaining strawberries.

2 Combine spinach, sliced strawberries, sunflower seeds, and feta. Toss with desired amount of dressing.

3 Split salad evenly between two plates and serve.

> **SERVING TIP** If desired, add 2 tablespoons walnuts (PowerFuel) to your salad for a heart-healthy crunch.

PER SERVING (½ recipe):

170 calories
5 g fat
1.5 g saturated fat
7 g protein
29 g carbohydrate
7 g fiber
15 g sugar
220 mg sodium

NUTRISYSTEM EQUIVALENT

Nutrisystem® Lunch Entrée +
1 Vegetable

Tomato and Red Lentil Soup SERVES 4

This simple and tasty soup is a great way to get in those extra servings of vegetables. The lentils add a nutrient-rich, satisfying source of SmartCarbs. Try it with a dollop of low-fat plain yogurt to enhance the creaminess.

PREP TIME 15 minutes   **COOKING TIME** 30 to 35 minutes

INGREDIENTS

1 medium onion, chopped

1 medium carrot, peeled and chopped

1 celery stick, chopped

2 garlic cloves, crushed

¼ cup water

2 teaspoons ground cumin

½ teaspoon paprika (optional)

One 14-ounce can no-added-salt diced tomatoes

1 teaspoon no-added-salt tomato paste

½ cup split red lentils

3 cups reduced-sodium vegetable stock

2 teaspoons sugar, or to taste

Freshly ground black pepper, to taste

PER SERVING (1 cup)

160 calories
1 g fat
0 g saturated fat
8 g protein
28 g carbohydrate
6 g fiber
9 g sugar
150 mg sodium

NUTRISYSTEM EQUIVALENT

Nutrisystem® Lunch Entrée

METHOD

1 Combine the onion, carrot, celery, garlic, and water in a large saucepan. Cover and cook over medium heat, stirring occasionally, for 8 to 10 minutes or until the onion is soft. Stir in the cumin and paprika (if using) and cook, uncovered, for 1 to 2 minutes or until the water has evaporated.

2 Add the canned tomatoes, tomato paste, lentils, and stock and bring to a simmer. Reduce heat to low, cover partially, and simmer gently, stirring occasionally, for 20 minutes or until the lentils are tender.

3 Transfer half the soup mixture to a blender or food processor and blend until smooth. Repeat with remaining mixture. Return the soup to the pan and simmer gently until heated through or until reduced to desired consistency. Taste and season with sugar and pepper.

COOKING TIP Yellow or green lentils could be used in place of red lentils if preferred. Lentils can be found with the dried beans at most grocery stores.

SERVING TIP Serve this soup with a small whole grain roll or a slice of whole grain toast for dipping (1 SmartCarb). Consider combining with a side of salad greens for a soup and salad combo that packs in a vegetable serving or two.

Rice and Beans with Chicken SERVES 4

This Latin-style dish is flavorful and nutritious. Brown rice offers fiber and B vitamins and pairs well with protein-rich chicken and beans. Prefer more heat? Add more hot sauce.

PREP TIME 15 minutes   **COOKING TIME** 40 minutes

INGREDIENTS

Cooking spray

8 ounces uncooked skinless chicken breast, cut into ¾-inch cubes

⅓ cup onion, diced

½ cup uncooked brown rice

1 clove garlic, minced (optional)

1⅓ cups reduced-sodium chicken broth

½ cup canned kidney beans, rinsed and drained

½ teaspoon hot sauce, to taste (optional)

2 tablespoons tomato paste

Black pepper, to taste

METHOD

1 Lightly coat the bottom of a medium saucepan with cooking spray and place pan over medium heat. When pan is hot, add the chicken breast.

2 Sear the cubed chicken breast on medium until outside of chicken is browned, approximately 2 minutes per side. Remove seared chicken from pot and set aside. Chicken will not be fully cooked, so keep separate from other foods.

3 Lightly coat the same pan with another layer of cooking spray and place over medium heat.

4 Add the diced onions and sauté for 3 minutes. Add rice, garlic, and chicken.

5 Quickly spray the chicken, rice, and onions with cooking spray and mix.

6 Add the chicken broth, kidney beans, hot sauce, and tomato paste to rice and bring to a boil. Reduce heat to low, cover saucepan, and simmer untouched for 30 to 40 minutes until all liquid is absorbed and rice is fully cooked.

7 Season with black pepper and additional hot sauce, as desired.

PER SERVING (¾ cup)

200 calories
2.5 g fat
0.5 g saturated fat
18 g protein
25 g carbohydrate
4 g fiber
2 g sugar
210 mg sodium

NUTRISYSTEM EQUIVALENT:

Nutrisystem® Lunch Entrée

SERVING TIP Serve in a 6-inch whole wheat tortilla (SmartCarb) for a satisfying lunch burrito.

Ham and Vegetable Frittata SERVES 4

Frittatas are great for using up whatever vegetables you have in the refrigerator or freezer. The trick is to keep it colorful. Try chopped cooked spinach or red bell pepper for a change. For a vegetarian version, simply leave out the ham.

PREP TIME 10 minutes   COOKING TIME 20 to 25 minutes

INGREDIENTS

1 small sweet potato, cut into ½-inch cubes (about 9 ounces)

1 cup egg substitute

2 tablespoons reduced-fat milk

2 tablespoons flat-leaf (Italian) parsley, chopped (optional)

½ cup coarsely grated reduced-fat cheddar cheese

freshly ground black pepper, to taste

olive oil cooking spray

3 ounces reduced-sodium, low-fat ham, chopped

1 medium zucchini, sliced into ¼-inch rounds

3 green onions, finely sliced (optional)

½ cup cherry tomatoes, halved

METHOD

1 Boil or steam the sweet potato for about 4 minutes or until just tender. Drain well.

2 Place the egg substitute, milk, parsley (if using), and half the cheese in a medium bowl and whisk with a fork until combined. Season with pepper and set aside.

3 Lightly spray an 8-inch nonstick, oven-safe frying pan with oil and heat on medium. Add the ham and zucchini and cook for 5 minutes, stirring often, or until the zucchini starts to soften. Add the sweet potato and green onions (if using) and cook, stirring occasionally, for 2 minutes.

4 Spread the mixture evenly over the base of the pan and arrange the tomatoes over the top, cut side up, pressing them gently into the vegetables. Carefully pour egg mixture and cook on low heat for 5 to 8 minutes, or until almost set.

5 Preheat oven to 300°F. Sprinkle the remaining cheese over the top of the frittata and place pan in oven. Bake for 5 to 10 minutes until top is lightly golden.

6 Cut into 4 even slices and serve.

COOKING TIP If you make the frittata a day ahead, store in an airtight container in the refrigerator.

SERVING TIP Make your own variation of this recipe with your favorite nonstarchy vegetables. Serve with a green salad.

PER SERVING (¼ of frittata)

160 calories
3 g fat
1.5 g saturated fat
16 g protein
18 g carbohydrate
3 g fiber
6 g sugar
460 mg sodium

NUTRISYSTEM EQUIVALENT

Nutrisystem® Lunch Entrée

Creamy Chicken and Corn Soup SERVES 4

This soup is a crowd pleaser. Top with reduced-fat cheese and serve with fresh vegetables or a green salad for a complete meal. Or add celery and carrots to the broth to sneak in some extra vegetables.

PREP TIME 10 minutes   COOKING TIME 15 to 20 minutes

INGREDIENTS

9 ounces trimmed chicken tenderloins or breast fillet

2 cups reduced-sodium chicken stock

3 cups water

3½ ounces short vermicelli pasta (see Cooking Tip below)

One 4½-ounce can no-salt-added creamed corn

Freshly ground black pepper, to taste (optional)

3 green onions, finely sliced on the diagonal, to serve

METHOD

1 Place the chicken in a medium saucepan. Add the stock and water and bring to a simmer over medium heat. Reduce to low and poach gently until the chicken is just tender (about 1 minute for tenderloins or 4 to 5 minutes for a whole chicken breast). Use a slotted spoon to transfer the chicken to a plate and set aside to cool slightly.

2 Bring the stock back to a boil. Add the vermicelli and boil for 6 to 8 minutes, or until al dente.

3 Meanwhile, use two forks or your fingers to shred the chicken. Add the creamed corn and shredded chicken to the soup and cook until just heated through. Taste and season with pepper (if using). Serve immediately, garnished with green onions.

> **COOKING TIP** If you can't find short vermicelli pasta, substitute any type of pasta or small noodle, like orecchiette.

PER SERVING (1½ cups)

190 calories
2 g fat
0.5 g saturated fat
18 g protein
24 g carbohydrate
1 g fiber
3 g sugar
330 mg sodium

NUTRISYSTEM EQUIVALENT

Nutrisystem® Lunch Entrée

Mix-It-Up Pasta Salad SERVES 1

Pasta salad can be a tasty and healthy way to satisfy your mid-day hunger. This recipe combines whole grain pasta, fiber-rich beans, fresh vegetables, lean meats, and fresh herbs and dressing. This portable dish can be conveniently made the night before for a quick, grab-and-go lunch.

PREP TIME 15 minutes   COOKING TIME 15 minutes

CHOOSE YOUR INGREDIENTS

1 SMARTCARB	1 SMARTCARB	1 POWERFUEL	1 VEGETABLE (or more)
½ cup cooked whole grain noodles, pasta, rice, or quinoa	½ cup beans: Chickpeas, red beans, black beans, pinto beans, navy beans, lima beans, fava beans, white beans, or kidney beans ½ cup peas ½ cup corn	2 ounces lean turkey, ham, chicken, roast beef 1 hard-boiled egg 1 ounce low-fat cheese ½ cup tofu	1 cup bell peppers, onions, broccoli, mushrooms, celery tomatoes, and cucumber

1 EXTRA

1 tablespoon of reduced-sodium, low-fat dressing or marinade.

A dash of sodium-free spices: basil, garlic, black pepper, mint, cilantro, thyme, lemon juice/zest, lime juice/zest, orange zest.

METHOD

Select your ingredients from each column, combine, and enjoy.

COOKING TIP ½ cup dry pasta yields 1 cup of cooked pasta.

NUTRITION TIP Cook your pasta "al dente," or to a slightly firm texture. Al dente pasta offers a lower GI profile than overcooked, soft pasta.

PER SERVING (2 cups)

340 calories
3.5 g fat
0 g saturated fat
28 g protein
53 g carbohydrate
16 g fiber
5 g sugar
360 mg sodium

NUTRISYSTEM EQUIVALENT

Nutrisystem® Lunch Entrée +
1 Vegetable + 1 Extra

AND SNACKS recipes

Healthy snacking may actually help you successfully manage your weight. By eating frequently and keeping yourself from becoming too hungry, you may be more likely to make better food choices and eat a proper portion at the next meal. So choose snacks centered on fruit, vegetables, whole grains, lean dairy, and meat—and monitor portions. The following recipes will give you a sampling of snacks and appetizers that will help satisfy your crunchy, savory, and even sweet snack cravings with a healthy option.

◀ Carrot and Raisin Salad, page 76

Carrot and Raisin Salad SERVES 2

This recipe tastes more like carrot cake than salad! Cinnamon and raisins enhance the sweetness of the carrots. This recipe is full of fiber and beta carotene and makes a great picnic dish.

PREP TIME 10 minutes

INGREDIENTS

½ teaspoon vanilla extract

2½ tablespoons fat-free or reduced-fat mayonnaise

½ teaspoon cinnamon

¼ teaspoon allspice

¼ teaspoon sugar substitute, or to taste

1½ cups carrots, shredded

3 tablespoons raisins

METHOD

1 Place mayonnaise in a small bowl.

2 Add spices, vanilla, and sugar substitute. Mix well.

3 Add carrots and raisins, and mix until well coated with dressing.

4 Serve chilled.

COOKING TIP For quicker prep, use prepackaged shredded carrots.

PER SERVING (⅔ cup)

110 calories
1 g fat
0 g saturated fat
1 g protein
25 g carbohydrate
4 g fiber
6 g sugar
220 mg sodium

NUTRISYSTEM EQUIVALENT

1 SmartCarb + 1 Vegetable

Three Bean and Basil Salad SERVES 9

This colorful salad makes a great afternoon snack or side dish to dinner. Beans are filled with lean protein and fiber to help fill you up. Store sealed in refrigerator for up to a few days.

PREP TIME 5 minutes

INGREDIENTS

1½ cups canned cannellini beans, drained and rinsed

1½ cups canned red kidney beans, drained and rinsed

1½ cups canned chickpeas, drained and rinsed

2 cloves garlic, minced

1 tablespoon lemon juice

2 tablespoons extra virgin olive oil

Salt and freshly ground black pepper

3 tablespoons fresh basil leaves, chopped

METHOD

1 Rinse all the drained beans well under cold running water. Drain.

2 Combine the beans in a large mixing bowl and set aside.

3 In small mixing bowl, combine minced garlic, lemon juice, and olive oil. Whisk well.

4 Combine olive oil and lemon juice mixture with beans and season with black pepper, salt, and basil to desired flavor.

> **SERVING TIP** This salad makes an easy and healthy side dish for potlucks and summer barbeques.

PER SERVING (½ cup)

160 calories
4 g fat
0 g saturated fat
8 g protein
23 g carbohydrate
7 g fiber
2 g sugar
25 mg sodium

NUTRISYSTEM EQUIVALENT

1 SmartCarb + Extra

Beet and Apple Salad SERVES 2

This sweet and crunchy salad makes a delicious appetizer or side dish to dinner, and it's quick and easy to prepare. Enjoy on a bed of arugula or mixed greens for a more filling snack.

PREP TIME 10 minutes

INGREDIENTS

2 tablespoons reduced-calorie balsamic vinaigrette dressing

2 teaspoons honey

¼ teaspoon nutmeg

¼ teaspoon allspice

¼ teaspoon cinnamon

1 small apple, core removed, sliced into small wedges

1 tablespoon low-fat feta cheese, crumbled

3 whole walnuts or 6 halves, roasted and finely chopped

1 cup canned beets, drained and cut into bite-sized pieces

4 cups arugula salad greens or mixed salad greens

METHOD

1 Mix together the balsamic vinaigrette, honey, nutmeg, allspice, and cinnamon in medium bowl. Add apples, feta, walnuts, and beets and mix well.

2 Using two bowls, place 2 cups of arugula or mixed salad greens in each bowl. Top greens with half of the beet, apple, and walnut mixture, and serve.

> **NUTRITION TIP** Arugula is a leafy green with a peppery flavor. It offers a good source of calcium and an excellent source of vitamins A and C.

PER SERVING (½ recipe)

160 calories
6 g fat
1.5 g saturated fat
4 g protein
25 g carbohydrate
4 g fiber
20 g sugar
260 mg sodium

NUTRISYSTEM EQUIVALENT

1 SmartCarb + 1 Vegetable + 1 Extra

To me, Nutrisystem isn't a diet—
it's a way of life that teaches you
to make healthy decisions.

—CONNIE N.

Easy Baked Pita Chips SERVES 2

These homemade chips are an easy to make snack and put almost-stale pita flats to good use. Whole wheat pitas offer fiber, vitamins, and minerals.

PREP TIME/COOKING TIME 15 minutes

INGREDIENTS

Cooking spray, as needed

2 small whole wheat pitas, cut into 16 wedges

1 teaspoon garlic powder

1 teaspoon dried basil

1 teaspoon dried oregano

1½ teaspoons olive oil

METHOD

1 Preheat oven to 350°F.

2 Place pita chip wedges on a baking pan lightly coated with cooking spray.

3 In a small bowl, combine all spices and dried herbs.

4 Using a small brush or small spoon, lightly brush a layer of olive oil on each pita.

5 Sprinkle spices and dried herbs generously on pita wedges and bake in oven for 10 to 15 minutes until crunchy.

> **SERVING TIP** Pita chips can be seasoned with a variety of herbs and spices. Store chips in an airtight bag or container.

PER SERVING (8 wedges)

110 calories
4.5 g fat
0.5 g saturated fat
3 g protein
17 g carbohydrate
3 g fiber
0 g sugar
150 mg sodium

NUTRISYSTEM EQUIVALENT

1 SmartCarb

Clockwise from top:
Easy Baked Pita Chips, page 81
Guacamole, page 84
Creamy Spinach and Feta Dip, page 83
Roasted Corn Salsa, page 87
Hummus, page 85

Creamy Spinach and Feta Dip SERVES 2

This savory dip is best served warm. It goes well with crispy, raw vegetables or Easy Baked Pita Chips (page 81) as a savory afternoon snack. Make a larger batch for guests.

PREP TIME 10 minutes   **COOKING TIME** 10 minutes

INGREDIENTS

Cooking spray

2 cups baby spinach

3 garlic cloves, minced

2 tablespoons low-fat cream cheese, whipped or plain

2 tablespoons reduced-fat feta cheese

¼ cup fat-free sour cream

1 tablespoon fresh chives, diced (optional)

1 cup carrot sticks

1 cup celery sticks

METHOD

1 Spray a medium sauté pan with cooking spray. Sauté the baby spinach and garlic together over low to medium heat for about 5 minutes or until the spinach has completely wilted.

2 In a small food processor or blender, puree spinach, cream cheese, and feta cheese.

3 Puree all ingredients until smooth and transfer mixture to a small bowl.

4 Add the sour cream and chives to pureed spinach mixture and serve warm with carrot and celery sticks.

> **COOKING TIP** Low-fat whipped cream cheese works best for this recipe.

PER SERVING (½ cup dip and 1 cup celery and carrot sticks)

130 calories
4 g fat
2.5 g saturated fat
6 g protein
18 g carbohydrates
3 g fiber
7 g sugar
320 mg sodium

NUTRISYSTEM EQUIVALENT

1 PowerFuel + 1 Vegetable

Guacamole 6 SERVINGS

Packed with the good fats, this dip is best eaten fresh, so make a smaller amount, and make it fresh each time. It only takes 10 minutes.

PREP TIME/COOKING TIME 10 minutes

INGREDIENTS

1 ripe medium avocado

2 teaspoons lime juice,
    or to taste

1 garlic clove, crushed

1 green onion, finely sliced

Freshly ground black pepper

Pinch salt (optional)

1 small ripe tomato, diced

1 tablespoon chopped flat-leaf
    (Italian) parsley or cilantro
    leaves (optional)

6 ounces baked tortilla chips,
    to serve

METHOD

1 Use a fork to mash the avocado flesh (make it as chunky or smooth as you like).

2 Add the lime juice, garlic, and green onion and stir until evenly combined.

3 Taste and season with pepper, salt (if using), and/or a little more lime juice.

4 Add the tomato and parsley or cilantro (if using) and stir gently to combine.

> SERVING TIP Guacamole also makes a great dip for raw vegetables, such as cucumber slices and cherry tomatoes.

PER SERVING (¼ cup guacamole with 1 ounce baked tortilla chips)

    140 calories
    7 g fat
    1 g saturated fat
    3 g protein
    18 g carbohydrate
    2 g fiber
    1 g sugar
    240 mg sodium

NUTRISYSTEM EQUIVALENT

1 SmartCarb + 1 Extra

Hummus SERVES 6

Made from chickpeas (garbanzo beans), hummus has all the nutritional benefits of legumes including a low GI. Keep a tub on hand in the refrigerator, as it is so versatile. You can use it as a dip for raw vegetables and crackers, or as a spread for sandwiches, rolls, and wraps.

PREP TIME/COOKING TIME 10 minutes

INGREDIENTS

14 ounces canned chickpeas, drained and rinsed

4 teaspoons tahini paste (optional)

4 teaspoons olive oil

2 tablespoons water

1 garlic clove

½ teaspoon ground cumin (optional)

¼ teaspoon paprika (optional)

1 lemon, juiced

Freshly ground black pepper, to taste

METHOD

1 Place the chickpeas, tahini paste (if using), olive oil, water, garlic, cumin (if using), and paprika (if using) in a food processor and blend until well combined.

2 Add lemon juice to taste and process until smooth. Add enough extra water to reach desired consistency.

3 Taste and season with pepper.

COOKING TIP Store in a sealed airtight container in the refrigerator for up to a week.

SERVING TIP Serve with raw vegetables such as celery, carrots, and cucumbers.

PER SERVING (¼ cup)

100 calories
6 g fat
0.5 g saturated fat
3 g protein
10 g carbohydrate
2 g fiber
1 g sugar
150 mg sodium

NUTRISYSTEM EQUIVALENT

1 SmartCarb

Nutrisystem changed my entire way of thinking
and taught me that it is possible to eat delicious food
and still lose weight!

—MARYAM S.

Roasted Corn Salsa SERVES 4

This authentic-style salsa offers a good source of fiber. Make the salsa ahead of time in larger quantities and store in the fridge for up to a few days. If you like more heat, increase the amount of hot sauce and enjoy with baked tortilla chips as an afternoon snack or appetizer.

PREP TIME 5 minutes   **COOKING TIME** 20 minutes

INGREDIENTS

½ cup corn kernels, fresh or frozen, thawed

Black pepper, to taste

Pinch of salt (optional)

Cooking spray, as needed

2 medium tomatoes, seeds removed and finely diced

¼ cup red onion, diced

2 tablespoons fresh cilantro, chopped

½ teaspoon hot sauce

1 teaspoon olive oil

1 tablespoon green onions (optional)

1 lime, for juice, as needed

2 ounces baked corn tortilla chips

METHOD

1 Preheat oven to 350°F.

2 If using frozen corn, pat dry with paper towels.

3 Season corn with a small amount of black pepper and salt and place on pan lightly sprayed with cooking oil. Roast in |oven for 10 minutes or until edges of corn start to brown.

4 Remove corn and allow to cool. Mix together corn, tomatoes, red onion, cilantro, hot sauce, olive oil, and green onions (if using).

5 Season to taste with fresh-squeezed lime juice and black pepper.

PER SERVING (½ cup salsa and ½ ounce baked tortilla chips)

110 calories
2.5 g fat
0 g saturated fat
3 g protein
19 g carbohydrate
2 g fiber
3 g sugar
70 mg sodium

NUTRISYSTEM EQUIVALENT

1 SmartCarb

Mushrooms Stuffed with Caramelized Onion and Red Bell Peppers SERVES 2

This vegetable-based appetizer is perfect to serve before a meal or at a party or as a side dish to a Nutrisystem® dinner entrée. Make this recipe up to a day ahead and place cooled mushrooms in a sealed container, and refrigerate. Reheat in the oven and serve.

PREP TIME 15 minutes   COOKING TIME 25 to 30 minutes

INGREDIENTS

2 teaspoons olive oil

Cooking spray, as needed

½ medium onion, sliced into long thin pieces

½ large red bell pepper cut into strips

1½ teaspoons dried basil

12 medium white mushrooms, stems removed and saved

⅓ cup whole grain bread crumbs

1 tablespoon grated low-sodium parmesan cheese

1 egg white

1½ tablespoons balsamic vinegar

¼ teaspoon black pepper

¼ teaspoon salt

1 tablespoon fresh basil, thinly sliced (optional)

PER SERVING
(6 stuffed mushrooms)

130 calories
6 g fat
1 g saturated fat
4 g protein
14 g carbohydrate
2 g fiber
7 g sugar
300 mg sodium

NUTRISYSTEM EQUIVALENT

1 SmartCarb + 1 Vegetable

METHOD

1 Preheat oven to 350°F.

2 In a medium sauté pan, add olive oil and small amount of cooking spray to pan and place over medium heat.

3 Add the onions, red bell peppers, basil, and mushroom stems and reduce heat to low. Caramelize the onions and mushroom stems for about 15 minutes on very low heat, and stir often to prevent burning.

4 In a small food processor or blender add the caramelized onions, mushroom stems, red bell peppers, bread crumbs, parmesan cheese, egg white, balsamic vinegar, black pepper, and salt together. Blend until all ingredients are mixed and form a sticky, crumbly texture.

5 Lightly spray a medium baking pan with cooking spray and place mushroom caps, stem side up, on the tray. Make balls with blended mixture to place inside the mushroom caps.

6 Bake mushrooms in oven for 10 to 15 minutes until caramelized onion mixture is golden brown and mushrooms are tender.

> **COOKING TIP** Use a small paring knife to remove mushroom stems.

Lemony Tomato, Mozzarella, and Basil Salad SERVES 4

This salad is best made with fresh tomatoes. Enjoy as a light snack, healthy pre-dinner appetizer, or as a side dish to a Nutrisystem® lunch entrée.

PREP TIME 5 minutes

INGREDIENTS

2 medium fresh tomatoes, cut into small wedges (about 4 cups)

4 ounces reduced-fat mozzarella cheese, fresh or shredded

4 teaspoons fresh basil, chopped

2 tablespoons reduced-fat balsamic vinegar salad dressing

Black pepper, to taste

2 whole lemons, cut in half

METHOD

1 Mix tomato wedges, mozzarella, basil, and balsamic dressing together in a bowl.

2 Squeeze desired amount of lemon juice on salad. Adjust seasoning as needed.

3 Split salad evenly between four bowls and serve.

PER SERVING (¼ recipe)

100 calories
4.5 g fat
2.5 g saturated fat
9 g protein
8 g carbohydrate
1 g fiber
3 g sugar
300 mg sodium

NUTRISYSTEM EQUIVALENT

1 PowerFuel

DINNER recipes

Dinner is most often the time that family and friends come together to eat. It is typically the meal that we spend the most time preparing. However, with our busy lifestyles, we may often resort to eating or ordering out, which can lead to poor food choices or overeating. Simple, quick to prepare meals can be healthy and satisfying—the following recipes will show you how. Keep your kitchen stocked with the essentials so you are not tempted to order take out. Refer to the sample pantry list on page 148 or the five-day sample menu and shopping list if you need more guidance.

Chicken Curry with Chickpeas, Squash, and Spinach SERVES 4

This savory dish offers ethnic flavors from the red curry paste and coconut milk. For a vegetarian version, try it with tofu. Serve with basmati rice (SmartCarb) and steamed green beans (Vegetable) for a complete meal.

PREP TIME 15 minutes   COOKING TIME 20 to 25 minutes

INGREDIENTS

1 small onion, finely diced

¼ cup water

3 tablespoons red curry paste, or to taste

4 boneless, skinless chicken thighs, trimmed and cut into 1-inch pieces

2 cups butternut squash, peeled, deseeded, cut into 1-inch pieces

One 14-ounce can no-added-salt diced tomatoes

1 cup reduced-sodium chicken stock

⅓ cup light coconut milk

One 14-ounce can chickpeas, drained and rinsed

3 cups baby spinach leaves

METHOD

1 Combine the onion and water in a medium saucepan and cook, covered, over medium heat, stirring occasionally, for 8 to 10 minutes or until the onion is soft. Add the curry paste and cook, stirring, for 2 to 3 minutes.

2 Add the chicken and squash and stir to coat with the curry paste. Add the tomatoes, stock, and coconut milk and bring to a simmer over medium heat. Reduce heat and simmer gently for 20 minutes or until the squash is just tender.

3 Stir in the chickpeas and spinach and simmer for 2 minutes, stirring occasionally, or until the spinach has just wilted. Serve immediately accompanied by the cooked rice and vegetables.

> **COOKING TIP** To reduce preparation time, purchase precut butternut squash.

PER SERVING (1 cup curry)

280 calories
7 g fat
4.5 g saturated fat
21 g protein
33 g carbohydrate
7 g fiber
7 g sugar
490 mg sodium

NUTRISYSTEM EQUIVALENT

Nutrisystem® Dinner Entrée

Baked Parmesan Crusted Fish with Easy Tartar Sauce SERVES 4

This recipe offers a tasty way to incorporate more fish, a lean source of protein, into your diet. This method of breading and baking fish is easy and healthy. Compared to traditional frying, it results in a dish lower in fat and calories, but just as flavorful.

PREP TIME 15 minutes   COOKING TIME 10 minutes

INGREDIENTS

2 tablespoons plain flour

Freshly ground black pepper, to taste

1 egg, lightly whisked

2 tablespoons reduced-fat milk

1 cup whole grain bread crumbs

½ cup finely grated parmesan cheese

1 pound lean skinless fish fillets, cut into 2-inch by 1-inch pieces (see tip below)

Olive oil cooking spray

Easy Tartar Sauce

3½ tablespoons reduced-fat mayonnaise

1½ teaspoons pickle relish

Garlic powder, to taste

Sugar or sugar substitute (optional)

1 teaspoon lime zest (optional)

METHOD

1 Preheat oven to 425°F and line an oven tray with parchment paper.

2 Spread the flour on a plate and season with pepper. Use a fork to whisk together the egg and milk in a shallow bowl. Combine the bread crumbs and parmesan, and spread on a plate.

3 Lightly dust the fish pieces with flour. Dip into the egg mixture, allowing any excess to drip off, and then coat well in the bread crumb mixture, pressing the crumbs firmly so they stick. Place the coated fish pieces on the lined tray.

4 Lightly spray both sides of the fish pieces with the olive oil. Bake for 10 minutes or until golden, crisp, and just cooked through, turning the pieces over halfway through cooking time.

5 To make Easy Tartar Sauce, combine reduced-fat mayonnaise and relish together and add garlic powder, black pepper, and sugar or sugar substitute (if using) to taste, and garnish with lime zest (if using).

PER SERVING (approximately 6 pieces of fish [or 3 ounces] and 1 tablespoon tartar sauce)

- 240 calories
- 8 g fat
- 3.5 g saturated fat
- 29 g protein
- 12 g carbohydrate
- 0 g fiber
- 2 g sugar
- 140 mg sodium

COOKING TIP Any lean white fish could be used in this recipe, including cod, bass, snapper, sole, grouper, flounder, or halibut. Ask for the best deals in the seafood section of your grocery store.

NUTRISYSTEM EQUIVALENT   Nutrisystem® Dinner Entrée

Vegetarian Tacos SERVES 6

Vegetarian tacos are a great way to incorporate beans into your diet. Beans are filling, low in fat, and are a good source of iron. Add chopped jalapeño to the tomato sauce if you like more heat.

PREP TIME/COOKING TIME 25 minutes

INGREDIENTS

2 cups Easy Tomato Sauce (see recipe, page 97)

Two 10½-ounce cans red kidney beans, drained and rinsed

1 teaspoon mild paprika

Freshly ground black pepper, to taste

12 taco shells

2 cups iceberg or romaine lettuce, shredded

2 carrots, peeled and coarsely grated

1½ cups coarsely grated reduced-fat cheddar cheese

METHOD

1 Put the Easy Tomato Sauce (page 97) in a medium saucepan. Add the red kidney beans and paprika and bring to a simmer over medium heat. Simmer for 10 minutes or until thick. Taste and season with pepper.

2 Assemble tacos, and top each with 2 tablespoons shredded cheese and desired amount of shredded lettuce and carrots.

> **COOKING TIP** Use reduced-sodium canned diced tomatoes in place of Easy Tomato Sauce for added convenience.

> **SERVING TIP** Serve with a tablespoon of guacamole (recipe on page 84) or reduced-fat sour cream if desired (Extra).

PER SERVING (2 tacos)

320 calories
10 g fat
2.5 g saturated fat
17 g protein
43 g carbohydrate
9 g fiber
8 g sugar
470 mg sodium

NUTRISYSTEM EQUIVALENT

Nutrisystem® Dinner Entrée +
1 PowerFuel

Nutrisystem really isn't a diet: it's about having a
healthy lifestyle and living that way for the rest of your life.
You learn how and what to eat.

—MICHAEL H.

Easy Tomato Sauce SERVES 5

This recipe is used throughout the book and offers an easy way to add vegetables to pasta, pizza, soups, stews, and even tacos.

PREP TIME 10 minutes   COOKING TIME 35 to 40 minutes

INGREDIENTS

2 teaspoons olive oil

1 small onion, finely chopped

2 garlic cloves, crushed

Two 14-ounce cans no-added-salt diced tomatoes and juice

2 tablespoons no-added-salt tomato paste

1 teaspoon sugar or sugar substitute, to taste

Freshly ground black pepper, to taste

METHOD

1 Combine the olive oil and onion in a medium saucepan and cook, stirring occasionally, over medium heat for 5 to 8 minutes or until onion is soft. Add the garlic and cook for an additional minute.

2 Add the tomatoes, their juice, and the tomato paste, and bring to a simmer. Reduce heat to low to medium and cook, uncovered and stirring occasionally, for 25 to 30 minutes or until thickened to a good sauce consistency. Taste and season with sugar and pepper.

COOKING TIP This sauce is very simple to make, and can be made in large batches and frozen.

PER SERVING (½ cup)

60 calories
2 g fat
0 g saturated fat
2 g protein
10 g carbohydrate
2 g fiber
6 g sugar
25 mg sodium

NUTRISYSTEM EQUIVALENT

1 Vegetable

Italian Meatballs with Spaghetti SERVES 4

A classic favorite the whole family will enjoy—now with whole grain pasta and homemade, lower-fat meatballs! Serve with a crisp garden salad.

PREP TIME 20 minutes   COOKING TIME 10 minutes

INGREDIENTS

12 ounces lean ground beef

¾ cup whole grain bread crumbs

¼ cup reduced-fat milk

1 small onion, coarsely grated

¼ cup roughly chopped flat-leaf (Italian) parsley or basil leaves

¼ cup parmesan cheese, finely grated, plus extra, to serve

1 garlic clove, minced

½ teaspoon chili flakes (optional)

Freshly ground black pepper, to taste

2 cups Easy Tomato Sauce (see recipe, page 97)

½ cup reduced-sodium beef or chicken stock

2 cups cooked whole wheat spaghetti, cooked al dente

PER SERVING (½ cup pasta, 3 meatballs, and ½ cup sauce)

> 250 calories
> 6 g fat
> 2.5 g saturated fat
> 26 g protein
> 26 g carbohydrate
> 4 g fiber
> 3 g sugar
> 75 mg sodium

NUTRISYSTEM EQUIVALENT

Nutrisystem® Dinner Entrée + 1 Vegetable

METHOD

1 Combine the ground beef, bread crumbs, milk, onion, parsley, parmesan, garlic, chili flakes (if using), and pepper in a medium bowl and use your hands to mix well until evenly combined. Roll mixture into 12 even-sized meatballs. Place on a plate or tray, cover, and set aside.

2 Combine the Easy Tomato Sauce and stock in a large frying pan and bring to a simmer over high heat. Add the meatballs in a single layer, reduce heat to low to medium, cover, and simmer gently, turning the meatballs halfway through cooking, for 8 minutes or until just cooked through.

3 Season sauce to taste with pepper and serve over ½ cup cooked whole grain spaghetti.

COOKING TIP You can prepare and cook the meatballs and sauce up to 2 days before serving. Keep in an airtight container in the refrigerator until ready to reheat.

NUTRITION TIP Pasta made from durum wheat is also a lower GI option, if you prefer it to the whole grain variety.

Mix-It-Up Stir-Fry SERVES 1

This stir-fry is easy to prepare, and the variations are endless! Lean meats, whole grain rice, and crisp vegetables are combined for a complete meal. The dish can be easily reheated for lunch or dinner the next day.

PREP TIME 10 minutes   COOKING TIME 10 minutes

CHOOSE YOUR INGREDIENTS

1 SMARTCARB

½ cup:

Rice: brown rice or basmati *or*

Noodles: egg noodles, rice noodles, cellophane noodles, soba noodles, plain or wheat pasta noodles

2 POWERFUEL

2 ounces of chicken, salmon or tuna, pork or beef *or*

3 ounces imitation crab, white fish, shrimp, scallops, lobster, or mussels *or*

1 egg *or*

½ cup tofu

1 VEGETABLE (or more)

1 cup (nonstarchy):

Peppers, onion, garlic, ginger, broccoli, zucchini, yellow squash, spinach, or mushrooms

1 EXTRA (optional)

1 teaspoon reduced-sodium sauce: soy sauce, hoisin, or teriyaki sauce

METHOD

1 Add ½ teaspoon vegetable oil to wok or sauté pan and place over high heat. Add meat and cook until almost done. Remove and set aside.

2 Add ½ teaspoon of oil or cooking spray and sauté the vegetables until cooked and crisp. If desired, add a small amount of water to help steam and cook the vegetables more quickly.

3 When the vegetables are cooked, add meat back to wok along with cooked cold rice or noodles. Add sauce and stir constantly until rice or noodles are hot. Serve and enjoy.

PER SERVING (1½ cups)

310 calories
9 g fat
1.5 g saturated fat
28 g protein
28 g carbohydrate
4 g fiber
1 g sugar
240 mg sodium

NUTRISYSTEM EQUIVALENT

Nutrisystem® Dinner Entrée +
1 Vegetable + 1 Extra

Salmon Cakes with Lemon Sauce SERVES 4

These cakes can be made with salmon or tuna. Both fish offer omega-3 fatty acids, which have been shown to promote heart health. This recipe pairs well with SmartCarbs like corn and peas. Or try the cakes as a salad topper.

PREP TIME 20 minutes   CHILLING TIME 30 minutes   COOKING TIME 25 minutes

INGREDIENTS

One 15-ounce can of cannellini beans, drained and rinsed

8 ounces cooked or canned salmon, skin discarded and meat coarsely flaked

2 eggs, lightly whisked

1 tablespoon reduced-fat plain yogurt

5 green onions, sliced thin (optional)

2 tablespoons chopped chives (optional)

1 teaspoon lemon zest

Freshly ground black pepper, to taste

1 cup white or whole grain bread crumbs

Olive oil cooking spray

Lemon Sauce:

½ cup reduced-fat plain yogurt

4 teaspoons baby capers, rinsed and chopped (optional)

3 teaspoons fresh lemon juice

PER SERVING (2 cakes and 2 tablespoons sauce)

260 calories
7 g fat
1.5 g saturated fat
26 g protein
23 g carbohydrate
5 g fiber
4 g sugar
400 mg sodium

METHOD

1 Preheat oven to 400°F. Line an oven tray with parchment paper.

2 In small food processor, blend beans until creamy or mash well with a fork or potato masher until creamy. Add the salmon, eggs, yogurt, green onions (if using), chives (if using), and lemon zest and mix until well combined. Season with pepper.

3 Shape the mixture into 8 even-sized patties. Spread the bread crumbs on a plate. Coat the patties with the bread crumbs and then place them on the lined tray and chill in the refrigerator for 30 minutes so they will hold their shape during cooking.

4 Spray the salmon cakes lightly with olive oil on both sides. Bake for 25 minutes or until golden and thoroughly warmed through, turning them halfway through the cooking time so they are crisp on both sides.

5 Meanwhile, to make the lemon sauce, combine the yogurt, capers (if using), and lemon juice and mix well. Cover and place in the refrigerator until required.

6 Serve the warm salmon cakes with the lemon sauce.

COOKING TIP To reheat cooked salmon cakes, place on a tray lined with parchment paper and then cook in an oven preheated to 350°F for 15 to 20 minutes or until heated through.

NUTRISYSTEM EQUIVALENT   Nutrisystem® Dinner Entrée

Soy and Sesame Marinated Chicken Drumsticks SERVES 2

Serve these savory Asian-style drumsticks with rice and stir-fried vegetables, such as snap peas. Serve with cooked brown or basmati rice (SmartCarb). This recipe can also be made with skinless chicken breasts if preferred.

PREP TIME 10 minutes   COOKING TIME 45 to 50 minutes

INGREDIENTS

1½ tablespoons reduced-sodium soy sauce

1 teaspoon canola or vegetable oil

1 teaspoon sesame oil

2 teaspoons pure floral honey

1 tablespoon fresh ginger, peeled and grated

2 garlic cloves, minced

4 chicken drumsticks

METHOD

1 Preheat oven to 425°F.

2 Combine the soy sauce, canola and sesame oils, honey, ginger, and garlic in a small bowl and mix well.

3 Place the drumsticks in a small ovenproof dish (just large enough to hold them in a single layer), pour the marinade over, and turn to coat. Bake for 45 to 50 minutes, basting the drumsticks with the juices occasionally, or until browned and cooked through.

> **COOKING TIP** To make ahead, combine the drumsticks with the marinade and store, covered, in the refrigerator for up to a day before cooking.

PER SERVING (2 drumsticks)

220 calories
9 g fat
2 g fat saturated
26 g protein
8 g carbohydrate
0 g fiber
6 g sugar
510 mg sodium

NUTRISYSTEM EQUIVALENT

Nutrisystem® Dinner Entrée

Grilled Salmon with Creamy Mustard Sauce SERVES 2

Salmon is an excellent source of omega-3 fatty acids and is easy to prepare. Pair salmon with rice (SmartCarb) and fresh steamed vegetables, like broccoli. The creamy mustard sauce, with a hint of citrus, complements the salmon nicely.

PREP TIME 15 minutes MARINATING TIME 30 minutes COOKING TIME 10 to 15 minutes

INGREDIENTS

¼ cup dry white wine

Zest and juice of 1 lime
(reserve ½ teaspoon zest
and 1 teaspoon juice for
Creamy Mustard Sauce)

¼ teaspoon black pepper

¼ teaspoon garlic powder

Two 4-ounce boneless
salmon fillets

Cooking spray

Creamy Mustard Sauce

½ tablespoon reduced-fat
mayonnaise

½ tablespoon reduced-fat
sour cream

½ teaspoon lime zest

1 teaspoon lime juice

1 teaspoon Dijon mustard

1½ teaspoons fresh dill, chopped
(optional)

PER SERVING (1 fillet)

210 calories
9 g fat
1.5 g saturated fat
25 g protein
3 g carbohydrate
0 g fiber
0 g sugar
160 mg sodium

METHOD

1 Mix together white wine, lime juice and zest, black pepper, and garlic powder in small bowl to make marinade. Add salmon to the marinade and refrigerate for 30 minutes to an hour.

2 When salmon is marinating, make Creamy Mustard Sauce by mixing together mayonnaise, sour cream, lime zest and juice, Dijon mustard, and fresh chopped dill in small bowl. After sauce ingredients are mixed together, cover bowl with plastic wrap and place in the refrigerator.

3 After salmon has been marinated for at least 30 minutes, remove from refrigerator and pat salmon dry using paper towels.

4 Heat outdoor grill or grill pan.

5 Season salmon with black pepper and garlic powder to taste.

6 Lightly spray grill with cooking spray and grill on high heat for 3 to 5 minutes on each side or until salmon is fully cooked.

7 Top salmon with the Creamy Mustard Sauce and enjoy.

COOKING TIP Salmon can also be seared in a sauté pan over medium to high heat for 3 minutes on each side, or until fully cooked.

NUTRISYSTEM EQUIVALENT Nutrisystem® Dinner Entrée

Easy Fried Rice SERVES 4

This Easy Fried Rice dish is lower in fat and calories and offers more veggies than the takeout variety! Add or substitute your favorite vegetables, such as zucchini, onions, and mushrooms.

PREP TIME 15 minutes **COOKING TIME** 10 to 15 minutes

INGREDIENTS

2 eggs

2 teaspoons water

4 teaspoons canola or peanut oil

7 ounces chicken breast, cut into ½-inch, small bite-size pieces

1 small red pepper, halved lengthwise, deseeded and thinly sliced

½ cup corn kernels, fresh or frozen

1 head broccoli (about 10½ ounces), cut into small florets

4 green onions, sliced thin (optional)

1 garlic clove, minced

½ teaspoon finely grated fresh ginger

¼ cup water, extra

1½ cups cooked brown or basmati rice

1½ tablespoons reduced-sodium soy sauce

½ cucumber, diced (optional)

METHOD

1 Use a fork to whisk together the eggs and water in a small bowl. Heat 1 teaspoon of the oil in a large nonstick wok or a nonstick frying pan over high heat until hot, swirling to coat the surface. Add the egg mixture and swirl again to make an omelet. Cook for 30 seconds or until the egg is just set. Roll the omelet up and transfer to a plate. Slice into thin strips and set aside.

2 Toss chicken with 1 teaspoon of the remaining oil. Reheat the wok until hot, add the chicken and stir-fry for 2 to 3 minutes or until just cooked through. Remove from wok and set aside.

3 Add the remaining 2 teaspoons of oil, red pepper, corn, broccoli, green onions (if using), garlic, and ginger to the wok and stir-fry over medium to high heat for 2 minutes, tossing frequently. Add the extra ¼ cup water and cook until the water evaporates and the vegetables are slightly tender.

4 Add the chicken, rice, and soy sauce and toss until heated through. Serve topped with the egg strips and cucumber, if using.

PER SERVING (1 cup)

280 calories
9 g fat
1.5 g saturated fat
18 g protein
28 g carbohydrate
4 g fiber
1 g sugar
260 mg sodium

NUTRITION TIP Basmati rice offers a lower GI than other white rice.

NUTRISYSTEM EQUIVALENT Nutrisystem® Dinner Entrée

Turkey Gyros with Cumin Tzatiki SERVES 4

This traditional Greek sandwich is served in a whole wheat pita pocket. The flavors of this recipe come from the savory flavors of the sautéed ground turkey and onions and the Greek-style tzatiki sauce.

PREP TIME 15 minutes   COOKING TIME 15 minutes

INGREDIENTS

Turkey gyros

12 ounces lean ground turkey

Cooking spray, as needed

1 medium onion, sliced into thin
    long slices

Black pepper, to taste

Garlic powder, to taste (optional)

4 small 4-inch whole wheat pitas

1 small tomato, diced (optional)

Lettuce, shredded (optional)

Cumin Tzatiki Sauce

1 medium cucumber, peeled,
    seeds removed, and cut into
    1-inch pieces

1 garlic clove

½ teaspoon ground cumin

2 teaspoons fresh chopped
    dill weed (optional)

½ cup reduced-fat plain yogurt

3 teaspoons lemon juice

PER SERVING (2 stuffed
pita halves and 3 tablespoons
tzatiki sauce)

    240 calories
    7 g fat
    2 g saturated fat
    22 g protein
    25 g carbohydrate
    4 g fiber
    5 g sugar
    230 mg sodium

METHOD

1 Place ground turkey in medium sauté pan and cook over medium to high heat. Sauté ground turkey until brown and fully cooked. Remove cooked turkey from pan and set aside.

2 Lightly coat the same pan with cooking spray and place over medium heat. When pan is hot, add onions and cook on low to medium heat until onions start to caramelize, about 5 to 10 minutes.

3 While onions are cooking, place cucumber, garlic, ground cumin, and dill in a food processor and pulse a few seconds at a time while scraping the sides of the processor. Cucumber mixture should be grainy in appearance, so be sure not to over-blend.

4 In a small bowl, combine the cucumber mixture with yogurt and lemon juice.

5 Just before onions are done cooking, add ground turkey back to the pan to reheat and mix with the onions. Turn off heat and season with garlic powder and black pepper if desired.

6 Slice pita in half and stuff each half evenly with ground turkey and onions, then top with cumin tzatiki sauce, diced tomatoes, and shredded lettuce.

COOKING TIP If preferred, substitute lean ground chicken or lamb for the ground turkey in this recipe.

NUTRISYSTEM EQUIVALENT   Nutrisystem® Dinner Entrée

Cheesy Tuna and Mushroom Rice SERVES 4

This easy one-pot meal can be made with ingredients right from your pantry. The flavors of this dish complement each other well, and tuna offers a great source of omega-3 fatty acids. A great recipe for tuna-melt lovers!

PREP TIME 10 minutes   **COOKING TIME** 25 to 30 minutes

INGREDIENTS

1 tablespoon olive oil

2 cups white mushrooms, sliced

½ cup diced onion

3 garlic cloves, minced

1 cup dry basmati rice

Two 5-ounce cans white chunk tuna in water, drained

2 cups reduced-sodium chicken broth, vegetable broth, or water

1 cup reduced-fat shredded cheddar cheese

Black pepper, to taste

METHOD

1 In a medium pot or a large saucepan with a lid, heat olive oil over medium heat.

2 Add the mushrooms and onions and sauté for about 5 minutes, until mushrooms and onions begin to soften. Add garlic and continue cooking for an additional minute. While the vegetables are cooking, rinse the basmati rice in a strainer until water runs clear.

3 Add the rice to the pot with the vegetables, and mix to coat the rice with oil to help prevent sticking.

4 After rice is coated with oil, add the tuna and broth and bring to a simmer and cover.

5 Simmer rice covered for about 20 minutes or until cooked. Sprinkle cheese on top of cooked rice, cover and heat for an additional minute until cheese melts. Season with pepper if desired and serve.

SERVING TIP Add 2 cups of cooked peas (SmartCarb) or an unlimited amount of your favorite nonstarchy vegetables.

PER SERVING (1 cup)

250 calories
5 g fat
1 g saturated fat
26 g protein
24 g carbohydrate
1 g fiber
1 g sugar
460 mg sodium

NUTRISYSTEM EQUIVALENT

Nutrisystem® Dinner Entrée

Grilled Eggplant Parmesan with Sundried Tomatoes SERVES 4

A vegetable-centered meal is nutritious and can be very filling. The delicious flavors come from the grilled eggplant, sweet tomato sauce, and tart sundried tomatoes, while the bread crumbs add a crispy texture. Serve with a side of whole grain linguine (SmartCarb) and a green salad.

PREP TIME 15 minutes   COOKING TIME 20 minutes

INGREDIENTS

Cooking spray as needed

1 large eggplant (1 pound), cut into twelve ½-inch-thick rounds

1 cup whole grain or panko bread crumbs

¼ cup reduced-sodium Parmesan cheese

1 teaspoon black pepper

1 teaspoon garlic powder

2 teaspoons dried parsley flakes (optional)

¼ cup sundried tomatoes, chopped into small pieces

¼ cup egg substitute or 1 egg

1 cup Easy Tomato Sauce (page 97) or 1 cup reduced-sodium tomato sauce

1 cup reduced-fat mozzarella cheese

METHOD

1 Heat a grill pan over medium heat. Heat oven to 350°F.

2 Using cooking spray, lightly grease the grill and brown each side of eggplant, about 3 minutes per side.

3 While eggplant is grilling, mix bread crumbs, parmesan cheese, black pepper, garlic powder, parsley flakes, and sundried tomatoes in a small bowl. After ingredients are mixed, add the egg substitute to the dry ingredients and combine to make a crumb texture.

4 Place grilled eggplants on a large baking pan covered with foil and lightly greased with cooking spray to prevent sticking.

5 Top each slice of eggplant with a thin layer of the bread crumb mixture and lightly spray with cooking spray.

6 Place in the oven for 5 to 10 minutes, until bread crumb topping slightly browns.

7 Top eggplants with tomato sauce and reduced-fat mozzarella cheese, and place back in oven. Bake for another 3 to 5 minutes until cheese is melted. Serve hot.

PER SERVING
(3 slices eggplant)

260 calories
7 g fat
4 g saturated fat
17 g protein
36 g carbohydrate
7 g fiber
6 g sugar
350 mg sodium

NUTRISYSTEM EQUIVALENT   Nutrisystem® Dinner Entrée

Spicy Chicken Wrap with Chipotle Ranch Sauce SERVES 2

The cooling ranch sauce helps balance the heat of this dish. If you like more heat, add more chilies to the sauce. Serve with crisp raw vegetables or a green salad.

PREP TIME 15 to 20 minutes   COOKING TIME 10 minutes

INGREDIENTS

8 ounces raw chicken breast, diced small into ½-inch cubes

1½ teaspoons diced canned chipotle chilies in adobo, seeds removed

1 lime, zested and juiced

1 garlic clove, minced

Cooking spray as needed

2 4- to 6-inch tortilla wraps

1 tablespoon salsa

½ cup shredded lettuce

Chipotle Ranch Sauce

2 tablespoons reduced-fat ranch dressing

½ teaspoon diced canned chipotle chilies in adobo, seeds removed

METHOD

1 In small bowl, mix together diced chicken breast, diced chipotle, lime zest and juice, and garlic. Allow chicken to marinate while making the chipotle ranch sauce.

2 To make sauce, mix together the ranch dressing and chipotle. Begin with a very small amount of chipotles and taste, and add more as desired. Cover and hold sauce in refrigerator.

3 Spray a medium sauté pan with cooking spray and place over medium heat. Add the diced chicken and marinade to pan and cook chicken until fully cooked (about 5 minutes). Remove the chicken from heat and set aside to make wraps.

4 To make wraps, lay out the tortilla wraps and place half the chicken, salsa, lettuce, and 1 tablespoon of the Chipotle Ranch Sauce in each wrap. Fold wraps and enjoy.

NUTRITION TIP Use whole grain tortillas to boost the fiber content of this dish.

PER SERVING (1 wrap and 1 tablespoon Chipotle Ranch Sauce)

> 240 calories
> 5 g fat
> 1 g saturated fat
> 26 g protein
> 21 g carbohydrate
> 3 g fiber
> 3 g sugar
> 360 mg sodium

NUTRISYSTEM EQUIVALENT

Nutrisystem® Dinner Entrée

Sweet Onion Meatloaf SERVES 5

Caramelized onions enhance the flavor of this home-style dish. For a simpler version, skip the caramelized onions and top with ketchup or your favorite tomato sauce.

PREP TIME 15 minutes **COOKING TIME** 50 minutes

INGREDIENTS

1 pound lean ground beef

¾ cup whole grain bread crumbs

¼ cup egg substitute
    or 1 whole egg

2 tablespoons reduced-sodium
    Worcestershire sauce

½ teaspoon garlic powder

½ teaspoon black pepper

1 teaspoon dried oregano

½ teaspoon salt or salt substitute

Cooking spray, as needed

1 large onion, sliced thin

½ cup reduced-sodium ketchup

¼ cup apple juice

2½ tablespoons balsamic vinegar

METHOD

1 Preheat oven to 375°F.

2 In a large mixing bowl, combine the ground beef, bread crumbs, egg, Worcestershire sauce, garlic powder, black pepper, dried oregano, and salt substitute. Mix all ingredients well using hands.

3 In a 9 x 5-inch loaf pan, spread the ground beef mixture evenly in the pan. Bake covered with foil for 30 minutes.

4 While ground beef is baking, spray a medium sauté pan with cooking spray and place over medium heat. When pan is hot, add sliced onions. Then reduce heat to low and cook onions for 15 minutes, stirring occasionally until onions start to caramelize.

5 Add the ketchup, apple juice, and balsamic mixture to caramelized onions. Mix together, and then turn off heat.

6 After the first 30 minutes of cooking, remove foil and drain any visible fat from the top of the cooked meatloaf. Top the meat loaf with the onion mixture and cover again with foil. Continue to bake the meatloaf covered for another 20 minutes. Allow meatloaf to cool slightly, and cut into 5 equal portions and serve warm.

PER SERVING (1 slice meatloaf)

240 calories
6 g fat
2 g saturated fat
22 g protein
25 g carbohydrate
1 g fiber
11 g sugar
450 mg sodium

NUTRISYSTEM EQUIVALENT

Nutrisystem® Dinner Entrée

Steak Quesadilla with Zesty Sour Cream SERVES 2

This Mexican-style quesadilla is stuffed with lean steak, sautéed vegetables, and melted cheese. The zesty sour cream provides some additional flavor. Black beans (SmartCarb) and a green salad pair well with this dish.

PREP TIME 10 minutes   COOKING TIME 15 minutes

INGREDIENTS

Cooking spray as needed

1 medium bell pepper, sliced into thin long slices

½ medium onion, sliced into thin long slices

6 ounces lean steak, sliced thin

Two 6-inch whole grain tortillas

½ cup reduced-fat Mexican-style cheese, shredded

2 tablespoons salsa

Zesty Sour Cream

½ cup reduced-fat sour cream

½ lime, juiced

1 teaspoon lime zest

METHOD

1 Preheat oven to 350°F.

2 Lightly spray a medium sauté pan with cooking spray and place over medium heat.

3 Sauté the peppers and onions for about 3 minutes over medium heat. Add steak and cook for an additional 3 minutes until steak is fully cooked and vegetables are soft. Remove from heat and set aside.

4 Lay both tortillas flat next to each other on a baking sheet. Split and add the cheese and salsa onto each tortilla, and split the cooked steak and vegetables between each tortilla. Fold each tortilla in half and place in the oven until the cheese melts and tortilla becomes crisp, about 5 minutes.

5 While quesadillas are in the oven, make the zesty sour cream by mixing together the sour cream, lime juice, and lime zest.

6 Slice each quesadilla into three wedges and serve immediately with zesty sour cream.

PER SERVING (3 quesadilla wedges with ¼ cup sour cream)

260 calories
6 g fat
1 g saturated fat
26 g protein
26 g carbohydrate
2 g fiber
10 g sugar
65 mg sodium

NUTRISYSTEM EQUIVALENT

Nutrisystem® Dinner Entrée

Tofu and Vegetable Yellow Curry SERVES 4

This flavorful recipe is the perfect one-dish meal, and you won't even miss the meat. Tofu is low in fat and absorbs the flavors of the yellow curry powder, cumin, and garlic. Add or substitute your favorite vegetables.

PREP TIME 20 minutes COOKING TIME 30 to 35 minutes

INGREDIENTS

½ cup plain flour

16 ounces firm tofu, drained and cut into 1-inch cubes

2 teaspoons vegetable or olive oil

1 green bell pepper, seeds removed and sliced into long thin slices

1 small onion, cut in half and sliced thin

1 head of cauliflower, cut into 1-inch pieces

1 cup frozen peas

2 cups reduced-sodium chicken or vegetable broth

1 teaspoon cumin

½ teaspoon black pepper

½ teaspoon salt

½ teaspoon garlic powder

3 teaspoons yellow curry powder

Cooking spray, as needed

PER SERVING (2 cups)

260 calories
9 g fat
1 g saturated fat
18 g protein
30 g carbohydrate
7 g fiber
5 g sugar
510 mg sodium

NUTRISYSTEM EQUIVALENT

Nutrisystem® Dinner Entrée

METHOD

1 Add flour to a large bowl, toss in tofu, and coat. Remove excess flour from tofu using a strainer placed over kitchen sink. Hold floured tofu in strainer until needed.

2 Add oil to a large pot or saucepan and place over medium heat. When oil is hot, sauté the green pepper, onion, and cauliflower for 5 minutes or until vegetables begin to soften. Remove from pot and set aside.

3 Lightly coat the same pot/pan with a second layer of cooking spray and place back on stove top over medium heat. Add the floured tofu and sear on all sides until browned (about 5 minutes).

4 Add sautéed vegetables and peas to pot with tofu. Pour in the chicken or vegetable broth and add cumin, black pepper, salt, garlic powder, and curry powder.

5 Bring liquid to a simmer and allow to thicken for about 15 to 20 minutes. Serve hot.

NUTRITION TIP Tofu is a lean source of protein, that is very versatile. Firm tofu works well in stir-fries and curries, while soft tofu can be added to smoothies for a protein boost.

SERVING TIP Serve curry over ½ cup of basmati rice (SmartCarb). Basmati rice has a lower GI than other white rice and easily absorbs the wonderful flavors of this dish.

Fiery Chicken Strips with Spicy Blue Cheese SERVES 4

This recipe is a healthy alternative to traditional fried hot wings. This spicy chicken pairs well with cool raw cucumber slices, celery, and carrot sticks.

PREP TIME 15 minutes   COOKING TIME 15 minutes

INGREDIENTS

1 cup plain whole grain bread crumbs (season with salt-free dried herbs of choice, if desired)

½ teaspoon cayenne pepper

½ teaspoon black pepper

½ teaspoon garlic powder

½ cup egg substitute

½ cup flour (season with black pepper)

Cooking spray, as needed

12 ounces chicken breast, cut into 12 long strips

Spicy Blue Cheese

¼ cup reduced-fat blue cheese or ranch dressing

1 teaspoon hot sauce or to taste

2 teaspoons Worcestershire sauce

¼ cup reduced-fat sour cream

Cayenne pepper, if desired

METHOD

1 Preheat oven to 375°F.

2 In small bowl, mix together bread crumbs, cayenne pepper, black pepper, and garlic powder.

3 Fill another small bowl with egg and another bowl with flour.

4 Spray a medium baking tray with cooking spray, and line up the three bowls in the following order: flour, egg mixture, and bread crumbs.

5 Dip chicken strips in flour, coat, and shake off excess. Next dip chicken in egg, and finally coat chicken completely in bread crumb mixture and place on baking tray.

6 Repeat this process until all chicken is coated with bread crumbs. Spray a light coat of cooking oil over breaded chicken and bake in oven for about 15 minutes or until golden brown and cooked through.

7 While chicken is baking, make the spicy blue cheese. Mix together reduced-fat blue cheese dressing, hot sauce, Worcestershire sauce, and sour cream, and add cayenne pepper to taste.

8 Serve chicken hot, accompanied by blue cheese.

PER SERVING (3 chicken strips and 2 tablespoons blue cheese)

250 calories
6 g fat
2 g saturated fat
26 g protein
22 g carbohydrate
2 g fiber
3 g sugar
450 mg sodium

> COOKING TIP Cayenne pepper is extremely spicy, so add in very small amounts until desired heat is reached.

NUTRISYSTEM EQUIVALENT   Nutrisystem® Dinner Entrée

Seared Pork Loin with Apple and Cranberry Compote SERVES 2

Sweet caramelized apples and cranberries complement the mild flavor of pork. Serve over brown rice with steamed broccoli and carrots.

PREP TIME 10 minutes   **COOKING TIME** 15 minutes

INGREDIENTS

Cooking spray, as needed

Two 4-ounce portions pork loin or other lean cut

1 teaspoon olive oil

½ small red apple, peeled, cored, and sliced into thin wedges

1 tablespoon apple juice

2 tablespoons dried cranberries

Nutmeg, small pinch to taste

Cinnamon, small pinch to taste

⅔ cup steamed brown rice

METHOD

1 Lightly coat a small sauté pan or grill pan with cooking spray and place on medium heat. When pan is hot add pork, searing each side until fully cooked (about 3 to 5 minutes on each side).

2 While pork is cooking, place oil in a medium sauté pan over medium heat.

3 Sauté the apple slices for about 5 minutes, until apples begin to soften and caramelize.

4 Reduce heat to low and add the apple juice, cranberries, nutmeg, and cinnamon. Continue cooking for an additional minute and turn off heat.

5 Plate the pork with the brown rice and top with the apple and cranberry compote.

PER SERVING (4 ounces pork loin with ½ apple and cranberry mixture, and ⅓ cup brown rice)

> 260 calories
> 6 g fat
> 1 g saturated fat
> 26 g protein
> 26 g carbohydrate
> 2 g fiber
> 10 g sugar
> 65 mg sodium

NUTRISYSTEM EQUIVALENT

Nutrisystem® Dinner Entrée

Sweet Apple Turkey Burgers with Apple Honey Mustard SERVES 2

Grilled apples and honey mustard add subtle sweetness to the mild flavor of the turkey burger. Serve with a crunchy slaw (Vegetable) and baked sweet potato fries (SmartCarb) for a complete meal.

PREP TIME 15 minutes **COOKING TIME** 15 minutes

INGREDIENTS

Turkey Burger

1 medium red apple, cored and peeled

6 ounces lean ground turkey

1 egg white

¼ teaspoon cinnamon

Cooking spray, as needed

Two whole grain hamburger buns

Apple Honey Mustard Sauce

1 tablespoon honey mustard or plain yellow mustard

1 tablespoon unsweetened applesauce

1 teaspoon honey

PER SERVING (1 burger)

280 calories
3.5 g fat
0 g saturated fat
27 g protein
41 g carbohydrate
5 g fiber
19 g sugar
330 mg sodium

NUTRISYSTEM EQUIVALENT

Nutrisystem® Dinner Entrée

METHOD

1 Using a cheese grater, grate or shred ⅓ of the apple into a medium mixing bowl. Reserve and set aside the remaining apple.

2 Add ground turkey, egg white, and cinnamon to the mixing bowl with the grated apple and mix well with hands. Form two even-sized patties and set aside on a plate.

3 Heat grill or grill pan over high heat. While grill is heating, slice the remaining apple into ½-inch slices. Sprinkle cinnamon on each side of apple slices.

4 Place the turkey patties and apple slices on the hot grill. Grill burgers on both sides until fully cooked, about 8 to 10 minutes. Grill apples until soft and lightly charred on each side, about 3 minutes total.

5 As apples and burgers grill, make sweet apple honey mustard sauce by mixing together the honey mustard, applesauce, and honey. Set aside.

6 Place the turkey burger in the bun and spread the apple honey mustard sauce on burgers. Top burgers with the grilled apples.

COOKING TIP To avoid a mess when grilling the turkey burger, use an outdoor grill or cast iron indoor grill to allow the drippings to drain from the meat while cooking.

Easy Baked Herb and Lemon Fish SERVES 2

White fish is low in fat and offers a mild taste that is enhanced by a simple mix of fresh herbs and lemon. This easy fish recipe can be made with any type of lean fish, including cod, bass, snapper, sole, grouper, flounder, tilapia, or halibut. Ask for the best deals in the seafood section of your grocery store.

PREP TIME 10 minutes COOKING TIME 15 to 20 minutes

INGREDIENTS

8 ounces lean, skinless fish cut into two even-sized portions

1 tablespoon olive oil

Black pepper, to taste

1 lemon, zested and sliced in half

2 cloves garlic

2 tablespoons fresh basil, chopped (optional)

2 tablespoons fresh chives, chopped (optional)

2 tablespoons fresh parsley, chopped (optional)

⅔ cup brown rice, steamed

METHOD

1 Preheat oven to 350°F.

2 Cut two pieces of tin foil that are large enough to fully wrap the two portions of fish.

3 Place fish in center of tin foil and brush each piece of fish with olive oil. Season fish with pepper and lemon zest. Squeeze all juice from each half of split lemon on both pieces of fish. Add the garlic and herbs of your choosing to foil and seal foil so fish is completely wrapped inside.

4 Bake fish for about 15 to 20 minutes or until fish is fully cooked. Serve fish with steamed brown rice.

> **COOKING TIP** Cook fish to 145°F. Fish should be opaque throughout when fully cooked.

PER SERVING (4 ounces fish and ⅓ cup rice)

240 calories
8 g fat
1.5 g saturated fat
22 g protein
19 g carbohydrate
2 g fiber
1 g sugar
210 mg sodium

NUTRISYSTEM EQUIVALENT

Nutrisystem® Dinner Entrée

DESSERT recipes

Everyone loves a sweet treat. Desserts centered on fruits, low-fat dairy, and whole grains in the proper portions can actually be a healthy snack. Our dessert recipes accentuate the natural sweetness of fruits while using low-fat yogurts to provide creamy textures when needed. In addition, we substitute in whole grains where we can to boost fiber and reduce GI. As a result, you get a satisfying balance of fruit, dairy, and healthful grains in the perfect portion to keep you on track with your weight management goals.

◄ Strawberries with Chocolate Peanut Butter Sauce, page 141

Apple and Pear Crumble with Vanilla Yogurt SERVES 8

Desserts centered on fruit and low-fat dairy products are often lower in calories and lower on the glycemic index (GI). Vary this recipe by substituting your favorite fruits or flavored yogurts.

PREP TIME 20 minutes   **COOKING TIME** 30 to 40 minutes

INGREDIENTS

2 medium apples (such as Granny Smith or Royal Gala)

2 firm ripe pears (such as Packham or Anjou)

2 teaspoons fresh lemon juice

Crumble Topping

½ cup rolled oats

3½ tablespoons all-purpose flour

½ teaspoon baking powder

½ teaspoon ground cinnamon

2 tablespoons canola or olive oil margarine

1 tablespoon brown sugar

½ cup pecans, chopped

1 cup low-fat, reduced-sugar vanilla yogurt

METHOD

1 Preheat oven to 325°F.

2 Peel, quarter, and core the apples and pears. Cut into thin slices, sprinkle with the lemon juice, and toss to coat the fruit. Divide among eight ½-cup ovenproof dishes. Set aside.

3 To make the Crumble Topping, process half of the rolled oats in a food processor until finely ground and resembling flour. Transfer to a medium bowl. Sift the all-purpose flour, baking powder, and cinnamon together into the bowl over the rolled oat "flour." Add the margarine and use your fingertips to rub in until evenly combined. Stir in the brown sugar, pecans, and remaining rolled oats.

4 Sprinkle the Crumble Topping over the fruit in the dishes. Bake for 30 to 40 minutes or until the topping is golden and the fruit is tender when pierced with a skewer.

5 Top the warm crumble with two tablespoons of yogurt and serve.

PER SERVING (½ cup crumble with 2 tablespoons yogurt)

> 170 calories
> 6 g fat
> 1 g saturated fat
> 3 g protein
> 26 g carbohydrate
> 4 g fiber
> 14 g sugar
> 80 mg sodium

NUTRISYSTEM EQUIVALENT

Nutrisystem® Dessert

Fruit Skewers with Yogurt Dip SERVES 4

A simple, healthy snack that can be made with your favorite fruits. Try variations with oranges, apricots, peaches, and mangos. This recipe makes about 8 skewers.

PREP TIME 15 minutes

INGREDIENTS

1 medium pear, cored and cut
    into thin wedges

½ medium banana, thickly sliced

1 apple, cored and cut into
    thin wedges

½ cup strawberries, hulled
    and halved

Yogurt Dip

1 cup low-fat, reduced-sugar
    vanilla yogurt

1 teaspoon honey

METHOD

1 Combine yogurt and honey to make dip. Cover and refrigerate until serving.

2 Thread the fruit onto short skewers and serve with yogurt dip.

PER SERVING (2 small skewers
and ¼ cup yogurt dip)

    120 calories
    1 g fat
    1 g saturated fat
    3 g protein
    28 g carbohydrate
    4 g fiber
    20 g sugar
    40 mg sodium

NUTRISYSTEM EQUIVALENT

Nutrisystem® Dessert

Dried Fruit Pillows MAKES 20

These home-baked cookies are sweetened with natural dried fruits. They will keep for up to a week in an airtight container at room temperature.

PREP TIME 20 minutes   COOKING TIME 15 minutes

INGREDIENTS

½ cup olive or canola oil margarine

⅓ cup superfine sugar or granulated sugar

1 teaspoon vanilla extract

1 egg

1¾ cups plain flour

1 teaspoon baking soda

Fruit Filling

¼ cup unsweetened apple juice

1 cup pitted dates, coarsely chopped

½ cup raisins

½ teaspoon ground cinnamon

PER SERVING (1 cookie)

130 calories
5 g fat
0 g saturated fat
2 g protein
21 g carbohydrate
1 g fiber
8 g sugar
105 g sodium

NUTRISYSTEM EQUIVALENT

Nutrisystem® Dessert

METHOD

1 In a food processor, blend the margarine, sugar, and vanilla extract together until combined. Sift flour and baking soda together. Add to the margarine mixture and combine using the pulse button, scraping down the sides of the bowl when necessary, until just combined. Turn onto a lightly floured surface and knead three or four times until dough is smooth. Divide the dough into two equal portions. Wrap in plastic wrap and place in the refrigerator while making the filling.

2 To make the filling, bring the apple juice to a boil in a small saucepan. Combine the dates, raisins, and cinnamon in a heatproof bowl. Add the hot apple juice and set aside for 10 minutes. Transfer the fruit mixture to a food processor and process until almost smooth. Transfer to a bowl.

3 Preheat oven to 400°F and line a large baking tray with nonstick baking paper.

4 Roll out one portion of the dough on a lightly floured surface with a lightly floured rolling pin to a 6 x 12-inch rectangle. Spread half the fruit filling over half of the dough (down the long side), leaving a ½-inch border around the edge. Fold the other half of the dough over the filling to cover, and press the edges together to seal. Cut into 1-inch-wide fingers. Put the cookies on the lined tray and place uncovered in the refrigerator while repeating the process with the remaining portion of dough and filling.

5 Bake for 15 minutes or until lightly golden and cooked through. Cool on tray.

> **COOKING TIP** If preferred, replace the dates with 1 cup of your favorite dried fruit, such as apricots.

Chocolate Chip Oat Cookies SERVES 20

Cannellini beans and rolled oats replace some of the margarine and flour in this recipe, adding fiber and protein and lowering the glycemic index. Dark chocolate contains antioxidants and provides rich flavor.

PREP TIME 15 minutes   **COOKING TIME** 15 minutes

INGREDIENTS

⅓ cup canned cannellini beans, drained and rinsed

1 egg

4½ tablespoons olive oil margarine

¾ cup firmly packed brown sugar

1 teaspoon vanilla extract

¾ cup dark chocolate chips or pieces

1⅓ cups rolled oats

¾ cup plain flour

½ teaspoon baking soda

METHOD

1 Preheat oven to 375°F and line a large oven tray with parchment paper.

2 Use a small food processor or stick blender to puree the cannellini beans with the egg until smooth. Set aside.

3 Use electric beaters to beat the margarine, sugar, and vanilla extract until smooth. Add the cannellini bean and egg mixture and beat until well combined.

4 Add the chocolate and rolled oats to the mixture and use a wooden spoon to stir in. Sift together the flour and baking soda over the chocolate and rolled oat mixture and stir until well combined.

5 Place heaped tablespoons of the chocolate and rolled oat cookie mixture onto the lined tray, about 2 inches apart (you will only use about half the mixture at this stage). Use your fingers to flatten each slightly. Bake for 15 minutes or until lightly golden around the edges and cooked through. Transfer to a wire rack to cool completely. Repeat with remaining mixture to make 20 cookies in total.

COOKING TIP These cookies will keep for up to 1 week in an airtight container at room temperature, but they will soften slightly.

PER SERVING (1 Cookie)

150 calories
6 g fat
2 g saturated fat
2 g protein
22 g carbohydrate
1 g fiber
11 g sugar
40 mg sodium

NUTRISYSTEM EQUIVALENT

Nutrisystem® Dessert

Frozen Berry Yogurt SERVES 6

This frozen yogurt is a tasty treat and low in fat. The natural sweetness comes from the fruit, yogurt, and honey. This recipe would also be delicious made with peaches or bananas.

PREP TIME 10 minutes   FREEZING TIME 7 hours

INGREDIENTS

2 cups fresh or frozen mixed berries

2½ cups low-fat, reduced-sugar vanilla yogurt

4 tablespoons egg whites, pasteurized

2 tablespoons pure floral honey

METHOD

1 Place the berries and yogurt in a food processor and blend until smooth. Transfer to a medium bowl and set aside.

2 Use electric beaters with a whisk attachment or a balloon whisk to whisk the egg whites in a clean, dry bowl until stiff peaks form, about 3 minutes on high speed. Add the honey a tablespoon at a time, whisking well after each addition, until thick and glossy. Fold into the berry yogurt mixture until just combined.

3 Pour the mixture into an airtight container and place in the freezer for 4 hours or until frozen. Use a metal spoon to break the frozen yogurt into chunks. Blend again in a food processor until smooth. Return to the airtight container and refreeze for 3 hours or until frozen. Serve in scoops.

COOKING TIP Make up to 2 weeks ahead and store in an airtight container in the freezer.

SERVING TIP Freeze ½-cup servings in popsicle molds for an on-the-go treat.

PER SERVING (½ cup)

130 calories
2 g fat
1.5 g saturated fat
6 g protein
26 g carbohydrate
2 g fiber
20 g sugar
80 mg sodium

NUTRISYSTEM EQUIVALENT

Nutrisystem® Dessert

Fruit and Nut Muesli Bar SERVES 15

A wholesome snack packed with fruits, nuts, seeds, and rolled oats. Each bar provides a great balance of protein, low GI carbohydrates, and heart-healthy fats. If preferred, replace flaxseeds with sunflower or sesame seeds. Dried cranberries or raisins would also be a good substitute for currants in this recipe.

PREP TIME 20 minutes   COOKING TIME 35 minutes

INGREDIENTS

1 cup rolled oats

1 cup Rice Krispies®

½ cup unprocessed oat bran

½ cup currants

⅓ cup dried apricots or peaches, finely chopped

⅓ cup almonds, finely chopped

¼ cup Brazil nuts, finely chopped

¼ cup sunflower seed kernels

2 tablespoons flaxseeds (optional)

¼ cup pure maple syrup

2 tablespoons olive or canola oil margarine

2 eggs, lightly whisked

METHOD

1 Preheat oven to 350°F. Line a brownie or square cake pan with parchment paper.

2 Combine the rolled oats, Rice Krispies®, oat bran, currants, apricots, almonds, Brazil nuts, sunflower seed kernels, and flaxseeds (if using) in a large bowl.

3 Mix the maple syrup and margarine in a small saucepan over medium heat until simmering. Reduce the heat and simmer for 1 minute. Add to the dry ingredients with the eggs and stir to combine evenly.

4 Spoon the mixture into the prepared pan and press with the back of a spoon to smooth the surface. Bake for 35 minutes or until set and golden on top. Cool completely in the pan. Cut into 15 bars.

COOKING TIP Store in an airtight container at room temperature for up to 2 weeks.

PER SERVING (1 bar)

160 calories
9 g fat
1.5 g saturated fat
4 g protein
17 g carbohydrate
3 g fiber
7 g sugar
25 mg sodium

NUTRISYSTEM EQUIVALENT

Nutrisystem® Dessert

Mango Milk Shake SERVES 2

By choosing reduced-fat varieties of milk and ice cream (or soy alternatives) you create a drink that provides sustained energy and boosts calcium intake but not saturated fat intake. If you opt for soy milk or ice cream, look for calcium-fortified varieties. If there's any left over, freeze as popsicles.

PREP TIME/COOKING TIME 5 minutes

INGREDIENTS

¾ cup fresh or frozen mangos, diced

½ cup reduced-fat milk or soy milk

½ cup reduced-fat, reduced-sugar vanilla ice cream or soy ice cream

METHOD

1 Place the mango, milk, and ice cream in a blender and blend until smooth and frothy. Pour into a tall glass and serve immediately.

COOKING TIP For variety, replace the mango with ¾ cup of any fresh or frozen fruit.

PER SERVING (¾ cup)

110 calories
1.5 g fat
1 g saturated fat
4 g protein
22 g carbohydrate
3 g fiber
16 g sugar
60 mg sodium

NUTRISYSTEM EQUIVALENT

Nutrisystem® Dessert

Cinnamon, Polenta, and Blueberry Loaf SERVES 16

Make ahead for a quick grab-and-go snack. The blueberries add color and sweetness but can be left out if preferred. Store in an airtight container at room temperature for up to 2 days.

PREP TIME 15 minutes   COOKING TIME 50 minutes

INGREDIENTS

Canola oil cooking spray

1 cup corn flour, sifted

4 teaspoons baking powder

2 teaspoons ground cinnamon

1½ cups cornmeal

½ cup firmly packed brown sugar

1¼ cups soy milk
    or reduced-fat milk

⅔ cup olive or canola oil
    margarine, melted and cooled

1 egg, lightly whisked

2 egg whites

1½ cups fresh or thawed frozen
    blueberries

METHOD

1 Preheat oven to 350°F. Spray a 4 x 8½-inch loaf pan with canola oil to lightly grease and line the base and two long sides with one piece of parchment paper.

2 Sift the corn flour, baking powder, and cinnamon into a large bowl. Stir in the cornmeal and sugar and make a well in the center.

3 Use a fork to whisk together the soy milk, margarine, egg, and egg whites in a medium bowl until combined. Stir in the blueberries. Add to the dry ingredients and stir with a large metal spoon until just combined.

4 Spoon the mixture into the prepared pan and bake for 50 minutes or until a skewer inserted into the center comes out clean. Stand in pan for 5 minutes before turning onto a wire rack to cool. Slice loaf into 16 slices and serve.

PER SERVING (1 slice)

170 calories
7 g fat
1 g saturated fat
3 g protein
25 g carbohydrate
2 g fiber
9 g sugar
210 mg sodium

NUTRISYSTEM EQUIVALENT

Nutrisystem® Dessert

COOKING TIP You can buy corn flour in health food shops, organic stores, and larger supermarkets.

Fruit Muffins MAKES 24

These naturally sweetened fruit muffins are ideal for a quick snack. Make ahead and store in an airtight container for a couple days or freeze in individual resealable storage bags.

PREP TIME 20 minutes   COOKING TIME 20 to 25 minutes

INGREDIENTS

2 cups self-rising flour

1 teaspoon baking powder

1½ teaspoons ground cinnamon

½ cup unprocessed oat bran

1 large ripe banana

1 apple (such as Granny Smith, royal gala, or golden delicious), unpeeled

1 cup fresh or thawed frozen mixed berries or blueberries

¼ cup pure floral honey

2 eggs, lightly whisked

¼ cup buttermilk

¼ cup canola oil

METHOD

1 Preheat oven to 375°F. Line two 12-hole muffin trays with paper cupcake or muffin liners.

2 Sift together the flour, baking powder, and cinnamon into a large mixing bowl. Stir in the oat bran. Make a well in the center and set aside.

3 Use a fork to mash the banana in a medium bowl. Core and coarsely grate the apple and add to the banana. Add the berries, honey, eggs, buttermilk, and oil and stir well to combine. Add the fruit to the flour mixture and fold together with a large metal spoon until just combined.

4 Spoon the mixture evenly into the lined muffin pans and bake for 20 to 25 minutes or until a skewer inserted into one of the muffins comes out clean. Remove from oven and transfer to a wire rack. Serve warm or at room temperature.

PER SERVING (1 muffin)

110 calories
5 g fat
0 g saturated fat
2 g protein
15 g carbohydrate
1 g fiber
5 g sugar
160 mg sodium

NUTRISYSTEM EQUIVALENT

Nutrisystem® Dessert

Nutty Oat Cookies MAKES 40

These cookies are rich in fiber and packed with nuts and seeds.
While they are very tempting, remember that a serving is 2 cookies!

PREP TIME 15 minutes   **COOKING TIME** 20 minutes

INGREDIENTS

1 cup plain whole wheat flour

1 teaspoon ground cinnamon

1¼ cups rolled oats

⅓ cup firmly packed brown sugar

¼ cup chopped walnuts

2½ tablespoons pepitas
(pumpkin seeds)

2 tablespoons sunflower seeds

4 teaspoons sesame seeds

7 tablespoons olive oil or canola
margarine

¼ cup reduced-sugar
maple syrup

2 tablespoons water

1 teaspoon baking soda

METHOD

1 Preheat oven to 325°F. Line 2 large baking trays with parchment paper.

2 Sift the flour and cinnamon together into a large mixing bowl. Stir in the rolled oats, brown sugar, walnuts, pepitas, sunflower seeds, and sesame seeds and set aside.

3 Combine the margarine, maple syrup, and water in a small saucepan. Warm gently over medium heat, stirring occasionally, until the margarine melts. Remove from heat and stir in the baking soda. Add immediately to the dry ingredients and stir with a wooden spoon to combine.

4 With damp hands, roll 40 walnut-sized portions of cookie mixture and place about 2 inches apart on lined oven trays. Flatten each ball to about 1½ inches in diameter. Bake for 20 minutes or until cooked through and beginning to darken around the edges.

5 Remove from oven and stand on the trays for 5 minutes before transferring to a wire rack to cool completely.

PER SERVING (2 cookies)

130 calories
7 g fat
1 g saturated fat
2 g protein
16 g carbohydrate
2 g fiber
6 g sugar
65 mg sodium

NUTRISYSTEM EQUIVALENT

Nutrisystem® Dessert

COOKING TIP Store cookies in an airtight container at room temperature for up to a week.

Strawberries with Chocolate Peanut Butter Sauce SERVES 4

This decadent dessert combines the flavors of chocolate and peanut butter with the sweetness of fresh fruit. Serve with strawberries, apples, bananas, or other fruits.

PREP TIME/COOKING TIME 10 minutes **COOLING TIME** 30 to 60 minutes

INGREDIENTS

4 cups strawberries, tops removed

⅓ cup low-fat milk

2 tablespoons reduced-fat peanut butter

¼ cup chocolate chips

METHOD

1 In a small pot, heat milk to almost boiling.

2 When milk is hot, lower heat to medium and add peanut butter. Whisk until peanut butter is totally dissolved.

3 Add chocolate chips to mixture, and whisk until chocolate is completely melted. Remove mixture from heat.

4 Pour sauce into a small bowl and leave uncovered in the refrigerator for 30 to 60 minutes or until sauce thickens.

5 When sauce thickens, serve or cover and leave refrigerated until needed. Serve with strawberries or other fruits for dipping.

> **COOKING TIP** Make the sauce ahead of time and store in the refrigerator until ready to serve.

> **NUTRITION TIP** Strawberries are an excellent source of vitamin C.

PER SERVING (1 cup strawberries with 1½ tablespoons sauce)

150 calories
7 g fat
2.5 g saturated fat
4 g protein
23 g carbohydrate
4 g fiber
15 g sugar
60 mg sodium

NUTRISYSTEM EQUIVALENT

Nutrisystem® Dessert

RESOURCES

STOCKING A HEALTHY PANTRY

Stocking a healthy pantry can help you be more successful with your weight management goals. Having healthy foods on hand may make it easier to incorporate them into your daily eating and may help reduce the temptation to make poor food choices. Strive for a balance of SmartCarbs, PowerFuels, Vegetables, and Extras that can help you snack or prepare meals that include lean protein, heart-healthy fats, fiber-rich grains, fruits, and/or vegetables.

While shelf-stable convenience foods are sometimes hidden sources of excess sugar and salt, you can make healthy purchases that fit with your weight management goals. Below are some tips to help you make smart choices and avoid healthy diet pitfalls:

- When choosing canned fruits, look for those canned in 100% juice or water and drain before serving.

- Choose **canned vegetables that are "low sodium" or have "no salt added,"** and rinse before eating.

- **Frozen fruits and vegetables can be just as healthy as fresh options.** The freezing process helps them maintain more of their nutrients over time. Just be sure that fruits contain no added sugars and vegetables are not laden with high-fat and/or high-sodium sauces.

- Milk is an important source of calcium and protein. Don't like milk? **Try calcium-fortified soy or almond milk instead.** Both can be used as a milk substitute, and you may prefer the flavor.

- Dry pastas are a family-friendly SmartCarb. Choose pastas made with durum wheat, which offer a lower GI, and prepare al dente. Whole wheat or other whole grain varieties of pasta may contain more fiber and protein per serving.

- **Dried and canned beans** are great low GI SmartCarbs. They can be added to stews, soups, pastas, salads, and even eggs for a fiber boost.

- **Buy meats in bulk and freeze individual portions** in airtight containers for up to 6 months. This can help you save money and control your portion size.

- **Dried brown and basmati rice** will also last a good while when stored in an airtight container and offer a low GI SmartCarb option.

- **Freeze grainy bread in individual slices if you can't finish the loaf in its prime.** Pop defrosted slices into the toaster for a quick and healthy breakfast.

- **Opt for breakfast cereals that are 100% whole grain and have limited added sweeteners.** These options will provide more fiber to help you stay fuller longer. Not sure if a cereal contains whole grains? Make sure that whole grains, such as whole wheat or oats, are one of the first three ingredients listed on the food label.

- Nuts and nut butters are PowerFuels that contain healthy fats and filling fiber. They also tend to have a long shelf life. **Choose unsalted or lightly salted nuts to help reduce sodium intake.**

- **Canned fish can be a convenient way to incorporate more heart-healthy omega-3 fatty acids into your diet.** Opt for canned salmon or tuna that is packed in water without added seasoning or salt. These fish are also available in shelf-stable pouches that eliminate messy draining.

- Dried fruits can be a great snack option. They typically last much longer than fresh fruit and contain just as many nutrients. **Be sure to choose 100% dried fruit, without added sugars or sweeteners, and limit serving size to ¼ cup.**

PANTRY LIST

POWERFUELS

Peanut butter or other nut butters

Nuts, unsalted

Canned tuna or salmon*

SMARTCARBS

Barley

Basmati or brown rice

Quinoa

Whole grain breads

Whole grain cereals

Whole grain pastas

Whole grain crackers

Whole grain English muffins

Couscous

Rolled or steel-cut oats

Canned beans, low-sodium

Dried lentils and beans

Sweet potatoes

Bananas

Dried fruit

Fruit canned in 100% juice or water

Unsweetened applesauce

VEGETABLES

Canned tomatoes*

Canned vegetables*

Onions

EXTRAS

Asian sauces* (ex: soy, teriyaki, chili garlic)

Dried herbs and spices (ex: paprika, cumin, oregano)

Dijon mustard

Fat-free salad dressing*

Vinegars

Reduced-sodium broths

Cooking spray

Vegetable oils (ex: olive, canola, sesame)

Marinara sauce*

Sugar-free preserves

Popcorn

*Higher sodium choice. Look for reduced-sodium options when available.

REFRIGERATOR LIST

POWERFUELS

Fat-free or reduced-fat yogurt

Fat-free or reduced-fat milk

Reduced-fat cheese*

Eggs or liquid egg whites*

Tofu

Boneless, skinless chicken breast

Cooked chicken slices*

SMARTCARBS

Fresh fruit or fruit slices

Berries

Hummus

VEGETABLES

Packaged salad mixes, lettuce, or cabbage

Baby carrots

Precut bagged vegetables (ex: peppers, onions, celery)

EXTRAS

Fresh herbs (ex: parsley, cilantro, basil)

Lemon juice

Lime juice

Low- or fat-free sour cream

Chili or curry pastes*

Fat-free whipped topping

Minced garlic or ginger

Pickles or relish*

FREEZER LIST

POWERFUELS

Boneless, skinless chicken breasts

Lean ground turkey, chicken, or beef

Lean beef and pork (loins and rounds)

Fish fillets

Shrimp and scallops

Veggie burgers

SMARTCARBS

Peas

Sweet potato wedges

Fruit, no sugar added

VEGETABLES

Broccoli

Spinach

Cauliflower

Brussels sprouts

Stir-fry vegetable mixes, without sauce

*Higher sodium choice. Look for reduced-sodium options when available.

SAMPLE WEEK OF DINNERS AND SHOPPING LIST

Planning is the key to healthy meal preparation. Still wondering how to get started? Below is a sample five-day dinner menu that incorporates recipes from the book as well as principles of the basic plating concept. Bring this shopping list with you to the store and then start thinking about next week's menu.

MONDAY	TUESDAY	WEDNESDAY	THURSDAY	FRIDAY
4-ounce grilled flank steak,* grilled asparagus, and whole grain dinner roll	Sweet Apple Turkey Burger with Apple Honey Mustard (recipe page 119), sweet potato wedges, and vegetable slaw	Steak Quesadilla with Zesty Sour Cream (recipe page 112), with green salad *Use leftover flank steak from Monday's dinner for quicker preparation	Tuna melt on whole grain bread, baby carrots and reduced-fat ranch dip	Ground turkey tacos on whole grain tortilla Shredded reduced-fat cheese & sour cream Sautéed onions and peppers

Shopping List (for one person):

7 ounces flank steak

7 ounces lean ground turkey

1 can of tuna

1 pack 4- to 6-inch whole grain tortillas

1 whole grain bun

1 whole grain dinner roll

Reduced-fat sour cream

Shredded reduced-fat cheese

Applesauce

2 apples

1 lime

2 onions

2 peppers

1 bag baby carrots

1 pound fresh asparagus

1 sweet potato

1 bag mixed lettuce

1 bag prepackaged vegetable slaw mix

May already have on hand:

Cooking spray

Salsa

Eggs

Mustard

Cinnamon

Honey

Reduced-fat mayonnaise

Reduced-fat Ranch dressing

MEASUREMENT CONVERSION CHART

1 tablespoon = 3 teaspoons = 0.5 fluid ounce

2 tablespoons = ⅛ cup = 1 fluid ounce

4 tablespoons = ¼ cup = 2 fluid ounces

16 tablespoons = 1 cup = 8 fluid ounces

2 cups = 1 pint

4 cups = 1 quart

8 cups = ½ gallon

16 cups = 1 gallon

1 pint = 2 cups

1 quart = 2 pints = 4 cups

1 gallon = 4 quarts = 8 pints = 16 cups

Nutrisystem has completely changed my perception of food and nutrition. Now, I think twice about what I'm putting in my mouth.

—JULIA G.

NUTRISYSTEM® TRANSITION AND MAINTENANCE PLANS

Nutrisystem offers Transition and Maintenance Programs to suit every lifestyle. Depending on the program you choose, you can incorporate Nutrisystem® foods every day or every so often. You will also receive access to portion control tools and cookbooks to help you practice the skills you learned on the program. As a Nutrisystem customer, you will also have unlimited access to our member website and complete menu of support options.

Use one or all of these flexible plans as you progress toward your goals!

- Did the structure of your 28-Day program work really well for you? If so, then the **Weekends On Your Own Plan** is for you. It's structured so you continue doing Nutrisystem Monday through Friday, while practicing healthy on-your-own eating on weekends. *You get 20 Nutrisystem® breakfasts, lunches, dinners, and desserts each month to help you stay on track.*

- If you're on the go seven days a week and can only slow down in the evenings, then the **Dinners On Your Own Plan** would be an ideal fit. With this option, you get a *Nutrisystem breakfast, lunch, and dessert each day (28 each), but prepare your own dinner each night.*

- If you are a person who needs more structure during the day, then you can opt for our **Just Lunches and Snacks Plan.** With this plan, you prepare *your own breakfasts and dinners, while enjoying a Nutrisystem lunch and dessert every day (28 each).*

- If you feel comfortable with minimized structure, you can choose our **Success a la Carte Plan.** With this choice, you will *order individual Nutrisystem® foods* (How many? That's entirely up to you.) at a special discount and get FREE shipping on any foods you order.

TRANSITION AND MAINTENANCE MEAL PLAN GUIDELINES

As you start to incorporate more of your own meals, self-monitoring becomes much more vital to Success. So use the handy charts below to learn when to adjust your daily eating or physical activity.

Change in Weight	Recommendation for CONTINUING TO LOSE WEIGHT
Lost >3 lbs./week	Add 1 daily SmartCarb or PowerFuel. If you continue at this rate, add another daily SmartCarb or PowerFuel until you're losing 1–2 lbs./week.
Haven't lost weight/ hit plateau	Diligently track your intake for the next week, making sure to include everything you eat and drink. If you still see no change, contact a Nutrisystem counselor for help.
Gained >1 lb./week	Subtract 1 daily SmartCarb or PowerFuel, and increase the duration and/or intensity of your activities. If this lasts for 2 or more weeks, contact a Nutrisystem counselor for help.

Change in Weight	Recommendation for MAINTAINING YOUR WEIGHT
Stayed within 2 lbs. of goal weight	Keep doing what you're doing! Keep eating this amount of food and monitor your weight every week.
Lost >2 lbs./week	Add 1 daily SmartCarb or PowerFuel. If this continues, add 1 daily SmartCarb or PowerFuel until your weight stays within 1–2 lbs. of your goal weight each week.
Gained >2 lbs./week	Subtract 1 daily SmartCarb or PowerFuel, and increase the duration and/or intensity of your physical activities. If this lasts for 2 or more weeks, contact a Nutrisystem counselor for help.

An Important Note About Physical Activity

As you approach your weight loss goal, it's important to be more active. Increasing the amount and intensity of your activity can help you be more successful at maintaining your weight loss. Strive for 45 minutes, or three 15-minute increments, of daily moderate or vigorous activity.

If you are very physically active, you may require additional calories, even if you are trying to lose weight. Contact a Nutrisystem counselor for help customizing your plan.

FOOD SAFETY: SAFE MINIMUM COOKING TEMPERATURES

Use a food thermometer to ensure that beef, poultry, seafood, and other cooked foods reach a safe minimum internal temperature. Refer to the chart below for the specific safe temperatures for each type of meat.

Remember, you can't tell whether meat is safely cooked just by looking at it. Any cooked, uncured red meats—including pork—can be pink, even when the meat has reached a safe internal temperature.

Finally, after you remove meat from a grill, oven, or other heat source, allow it to rest for the specified amount of time. During the rest time, the temperature of the food remains constant or continues to rise, which destroys harmful germs.

CATEGORY	FOOD	TEMPERATURE °F	REST TIME
GROUND MEAT & MEAT MIXTURES	Beef, pork, veal, lamb	160	None
	Turkey, chicken	165	None
FRESH BEEF, VEAL, LAMB	Steaks, roasts, chops	145	3 minutes
POULTRY	Chicken & turkey, whole	165	None
	Poultry breasts, roasts	165	None
	Poultry thighs, legs, wings	165	None
	Duck & goose	165	None
	Stuffing (cooked alone or in bird)	165	None
PORK & HAM	Fresh pork	145	3 minutes
	Fresh ham (raw)	145	3 minutes
	Precooked ham (to reheat)	140	None
EGGS & EGG DISHES	Eggs	Cook until yolk and white are firm	None
	Egg dishes	160	None
LEFTOVERS & CASSEROLES	Leftovers	165	None
	Casseroles	165	None
SEAFOOD	Fin fish	145 or cook until flesh is opaque and separates easily with a fork	None
	Shrimp, lobster, crabs	Cook until flesh is pearly and opaque	None
	Clams, oysters, mussels	Cook until shells open during cooking	None
	Scallops	Cook until flesh is milky white or opaque and firm	None

Source: The United States Department of Health and Human Services, www.foodsafety.gov

ACKNOWLEDGMENTS

Simple Success includes Nutrisystem-developed recipes, as well as recipes adapted from the *New Glucose Revolution Low GI Family Cookbook* and the *New Glucose Revolution Life Plan*. All of the recipes fit within the Nutrisystem® weight loss program and can be tailored to an individual maintaining his or her weight. The recipes are simple enough to prepare during the week but special enough to serve guests.

Nutrisystem would like to acknowledge the contributions of Max Sugarman. Max is a graduate of Johnson and Wales University in Providence, RI. He has a Bachelor of Science degree in culinary nutrition and an Associate Applied Science degree in culinary arts. Max, along with the Nutrisystem registered dietitians and Food and Product Development Team worked closely to develop recipes that comply with the Nutrisystem® weight management approach.

Nutrisystem also thanks the New Glucose Revolution Team for their continued support and partnership. The New Glucose Revolution Team, Jennie Brand-Miller, Kaye Foster-Powell, and Joanna McMillan, are renowned glycemic index (GI) experts. They have published numerous books and cookbooks that have empowered people around the world to follow a low GI diet and prepare more healthy and delicious foods. Now as a partner with Nutrisystem, Inc., a leader in weight loss programs, the team brings their simple and delicious recipes to those seeking to manage their weight the Nutrisystem way.

All the recipes included in this book deliver an optimal blend of nutrient-dense ingredients including high fiber, low GI "good" carbohydrates, high-quality lean proteins, heart-healthy unsaturated fats, as well as vitamin- and mineral-rich fruits and vegetables. The recipe serving sizes help reinforce proper portion sizes, which is critical for weight management and a key component of the Nutrisystem® program. Best of all, the recipes and resources in this book are designed for simplicity and convenience—after all, that's what we're known for here at Nutrisystem. (Check out pages 20–33 for our no-nonsense plating guide, which shows you how to create quick and healthy entrée combinations.)

INDEX